Women of Silence

Grace Adamson

Women of Silence

Reconnecting with the Emotional Healing of Breast Cancer

The essential handbook for all women:

* ❋ Illness prevention and health promotion
* ❋ Breast health and healing
* ❋ Self-discovery
* ❋ Understanding the power of emotions
* ❋ Connecting body, mind, emotion and spirit

Grace Adamson

Highclere Limited
United Kingdom

First published in the UK 2003
by Highclere Limited, Taunton, Somerset, UK

British Library Cataloguing-in-Publication Data
A catalogue record for this book is available from the British Library

ISBN: 0-9545480-0-0

Cover design by Kate Merrifield
Photography by John Melville
Sub-edited by Anne Malandine
Typeset in the UK by Text 2 Text Limited, Devon
Printed in the UK by MPG Books Limited, Cornwall

Women of Silence

Women of Silence, gentle and strong,
Tell me your path, where it first went wrong.
Tell me your story, how you've coped with your life.
Tell me about all the trouble and the strife.

I see how you've coped, withholding the pain,
I feel your soul weeping and yet you refrain
From sharing your losses, your grief and your fears
But you know, they multiply over the years.

Until one day your inner wisdom says "no more".
And you awake with an illness, a fiery core
That's fuelled by a lifestyle out of control,
Too much held too often has taken its toll.

It's time to rethink, reassess how it's been
And develop a strategy previously unseen.
There is a way to heal with heart and great passion.
Let go of withholding that was always your fashion.

Nurture yourself and make yourself whole.
Live your life fully and realise your goals.
Women of Silence, gentle and strong,
Find the courage to heal, and to sing your heart's song.

© Grace Adamson 2003

Dedicated to Guy
"The Wind Beneath my Wings!"

Contents

By the same author:

Women of Silence: The Emotional Healing of Breast Cancer

Foreword

Grace Adamson is a woman who writes from a lifetime of experience, both personal and professional. Her commitment to support cancer patients has stretched from the Southern to the Northern hemisphere.

Her book is timely and comes at a time when the WHO is emphasising prevention as cancer rates continue to soar. This book is not about alternatives, but it is a well considered approach that provides the bridge between the medical and the emotional issues surrounding breast cancer.

Grace wants women to be innovative and proactive, so that the emphasis is on self-care. It is not just about providing women with practical well-proven methods that work, but it is also about asking women to examine how they live their lives. It is about encouraging women to "sing" again; rather than fall victim to their illness.

As a consultant oncologist, I am very aware that emotional and lifestyle issues play a big part in the management of cancer. Grace's commitment to helping cancer patients is inspiring.

Professor Neville Davidson FRCP FRCR

Professor in Clinical Oncology, Broomfield Hospital.
Chairman HEAL Cancer Charity and
Helen Rollason Cancer Care Centre Appeal.

Acknowledgements

The first **Women of Silence: The Emotional Healing of Breast Cancer** was penned in 1994 as a result of my many years of therapeutic experience of working with women who were dealing with breast cancer. At that time, **Women of Silence** was a book that not only asked to be written, but demanded to written. There was clearly an absence of material that discussed the experience and the journey of what it was like to be walking, and to have walked, the path of uncertainty that a diagnosis of breast cancer brings. The challenge for me then was to put pen to paper amidst a busy family and working life and draw upon the enormous amount of material that patients had shared with me. However it was not until a car accident gave me the "gift" of a nasty whiplash injury and therefore an enforced holiday that the manuscript began to take physical form. So often uninvited change brings gifts in unfamiliar packages! I also did not realize that **Women of Silence** would be so pivotal in my own life. It evolved as a book not only about breast cancer; but about women's lives, women's journeys and women's wisdom, and in this case, born out of the experience of a great life teacher called breast cancer.

Ironically, **"Women of Silence: Reconnecting with the Emotional Healing of Breast Cancer"** comes at yet another time of enormous shifts and changes in my life. So, for me both the production and ongoing process of this book has been an extraordinary learning time. First and foremost the most important people to acknowledge and thank are the women who have trusted in me to share their life journey for a while and who have generously allowed me to use their stories as a springboard for learning and teaching.

There are some special and extraordinary people whom I wish to acknowledge; people who have appeared on the stage of my life as if exactly on cue.

To Pat Coleby, salt of the earth and tower of strength — thank you for being there and supporting me as carer-to-carer so many years ago.

I have been more than fortunate to have many wise and empowered women mentors in my life. My elusive friend Norma, whose love radiates out to me wherever I am in the world and who appears or writes exactly when she is needed. She has been a catalyst for my understanding of healing on many levels. She taught me how to trust raw instinct and intuition and reminded me to connect with my soul.

My dear friend, Dorothy Hall, an exceptional healer, herbalist, reader of people and a woman of high integrity, good humour and wisdom. Dorothy's teaching and friendship has had a huge impact on my life and I thankfully acknowledge the value of her teachings and for showing me the way to practise *herbal medicine as an art.*

Ilana Rubenfeld, again a teacher, friend and colleague. A life devoted to assisting people with therapeutic change, Ilana is known as the *doyenne* in her field of working with mind, body, emotions and spirit. She showed me the way of true self-care and awareness that has literally saved my life throughout the traumas of the nineties. Thank you for your being and sharing and your trusted company as a woman.

Time passes by and life brings many changes — and not only for books! Some life changes are invited and can be prepared for and some are uninvited, surprise us and remind us of the vulnerability of being human. Three years after the first edition of **Women of Silence** was published, my partner of 23 years abruptly ended our marriage. This culminated in a cascade of major personal changes and health issues for me. During this time of chaos my thanks go to my children and to my two friends Helen Wallis and Helen Marguiles who helped with the practicalities of food, house and general survival issues.

A very special thanks to Dr John Sullivan and Mr Neil Collier from The Freemasons Hospital in Melbourne, Australia for their expertise, skill and support that has enabled me to survive. To all my Dutch friends, Bibi and Nico Brouwer, Hanneke and Paul Hoekstra, Bart and Manec van der Lugt and family, thank you for genuinely supporting me before and throughout my quest for health and especially for welcoming me into your respective homes and families. I could not have done it without you! Immeasurable thanks must go to Dr Mark Vierhout and Dr Rudolph Schouten and his team especially Marijke Slieker at Erasmus University Hospital in Rotterdam, The Netherlands. What can I say to you all? Thank you for giving me my life back. Of most importance is the return of my life quality without an ileostomy or colostomy bag!

To the *Medical Journal of Australia* for their permission to quote from studies and to Allan B. Chinen MD, author of *Once Upon a Midlife*, who kindly gave permission to reproduce a story from his book — thank you.

Last but certainly not least, my gratitude goes to my partner of three years who more recently became my husband. He has supplied me with loads of love, enthusiasm, encouragement, support and trust for which I sincerely thank him. Being very ill when we met, he was undaunted by the challenge that I was facing in my recovery. He has helped me steer through some very troubled waters as I tried to adjust to my new lifestyle and to the life-altering situations that having a stoma brings. Importantly, he has believed in the necessity of my continued work in the field of women's health. Without that loving support, I may not have survived to pursue my recovery, continue my work and write this book.

The stories mentioned in this book are factual, however, patients' names have been changed to respect their privacy.

Preface

Women *are* different to men. This is not earth shattering news! The differences are often joked about and some have gone as far as to say that we have even come from different planets! However, of particular interest to me regarding this issue, concerns the field of medicine and particularly cancer medicine. With few exceptions most oncology practitioners are male. The female side, the hormonal side associated with how women handle emotions is outside the expertise of most oncology practitioners. Indeed it is *not* the job that they are there to do. What you do need is a precise and caring technician to help with the physical aspects of cancer. There is enormous skill, precision and care demanded in oncology practice — qualities which are, of course, essential as well as all consuming. However it is helpful if oncologists can encourage, support or be an advocate for you in your choice to seek complementary and supportive care.

There is a lack of real understanding of the communication styles and unique emotional styles of the genders. This becomes especially evident when we are dealing with issues of women's health, gynaecology and oncology. The diagnostics and treatments for these issues can be not only personally invasive, but the long term impacts of altered body image, self-esteem, early menopause and the restrictions resulting from radiotherapy can have a lasting impact on life quality.

The communication exchanged between women and their doctors is an area in need of much improvement. It highlights the need for adjuvant psychological, emotional and spiritual care as a part of integrated cancer management. Traumatised women often remain silent, overwhelmed and obedient in the consulting room.

Women are biologically, hormonally and ecologically sensitive. Like the tides we are governed by the phases of the moon. We even synchronise our cycles easily with other women who are in our work or living space. We like to connect, network, enjoy consensus and have an innate desire for intimacy and interdependence. Women need to be heard, listened to, understood and empathised with first and foremost.

Importantly this dictates care of THE PERSON; not treatment of THE CELLS.

But there is no time for this in the highly proactive and solution driven world of oncology where practitioners work under the pressure of the ever-increasing swell of patient numbers. So we need to find a solution that offers the opportunity for personal expression whilst obtaining the best of medical care. The gap between the two is obvious, but can be bridged by the mutual understanding of where the other is coming from.

Attention to understanding emotions is pivotal to women's health. Especially in helping them to find their voice so that they can liberate themselves from bottled-up feelings and emotions.

Therefore there is a need to speak about the unspeakable. *There is a need to break the silence before it breaks you!*

That is what this book is all about. I have seen enough evidence-based results to believe that for illness, early intervention with methods that address the emotional aspects, is essential for healing and recovery. Also finding peace from emotional and spiritual pain can provide us with a good experience of the process of death and of death itself. Anecdotally I have seen less recurrence and better management of serious illness in women who have followed this approach. Young, healthy women who are just beginning their journey can benefit enormously from the wisdom of getting to know their emotional patterns. For young men too, we need to be encouraging the promotion of healthy emotions rather than being so totally focused on dealing with the aftermath, such as depression, anxiety and drug addictions. A compassionate society interested in humanitarian issues needs to address this problem. For cancer patients, unresolved emotional pain is the root cause of most suffering. Its lack of resolve does exacerbate physical pain.

Just as we have programmes for healthy eating, I would like to see *Centres of Excellence* and more programmes developed that educate, teach and deal with the emotional health and wellbeing of the community at large.

Introduction: Understanding the Motion of Emotion

The emotional aspects of a woman's life are often neglected in conventional medicine as we know it today. In my own clinical work with cancer patients, especially women with breast cancer, the similarities in their emotional life histories have been too obvious to ignore — this is the hidden side of cancer. Although there are visible lumps on and in the body, these symptoms may actually have their origins deep within the soul, where the creative threads of life dwell; the place from which we can either live or not live our truth. When there are blocks in the creative flow of a woman's life and when the expression of that creativity is blocked, her creative energy can become stultified and movement of emotion and feeling ceases. The effect is that women can become frustrated and blocked from responding to life. As a cover or alias a false self is created; the false self rides over the top of situations pretending that all is well when in reality it is not. It then becomes harder for a woman to live her truth even though she knows what it is and how she would like to be. Therein lies the fuel for tremendous personal conflict.

If one takes the time to listen to the life stories of women with breast cancer we often discover a history of unresolved emotional pain and unresolved grief or trauma throughout their lives. Another common denominator has been the identification eighteen months to two years prior to diagnosis, of a key traumatic event that occurred in their lives. Women know and remember these times and may describe feelings of shock, inability to cope, denial and silence as if a part of them has been frozen and suspended in time.

When you drop a stone into a pool of water there is a ripple effect — circles radiate out across the water. Using that analogy, I believe that many of the modern orthodox and alternative treatments for cancer are focused on the "ripples" only. To me it appears that they are failing to see that the ripples are a consequence, or a symptom, of a greater block and that block is like the original stone that was dropped into the water. If we observe this mechanism and can find the central issue that created the pattern, we can understand that the ripples of our life are not causes but consequences. By going back to the stone, the originator, we help to fully heal the ripples. This then becomes healing from the inside out.

Patients who consciously participate in their own healing with this type of idea as their premise, tend to experience a marked increase in the effectiveness of any other healing modalities they are using. This applies to all treatments including chemotherapy, radiotherapy, alternative remedies or a combination of them all. Those who can reframe their illness and develop personal awareness and understanding can gain a sense of empowerment that is real and personally sustaining. Some sense of self-mastery is important throughout the management of cancer. This highlights the difference between being a victim of cancer or becoming a victor.

Women can seize the opportunity to move forward; rather than experiencing their cancer as just plain bad luck they can see a connection between the events in their life and the way they have coped. This is quite different from the premise that women have caused their cancer. My understanding of this is that people respond to life's events in the best way they know how. The illness can be a wake up call inviting you to look at how you have been playing the hand of cards that life dealt to you. Spiritual and emotional mettle is borne out of learning to play a bad hand of cards well. The results bring about healing;

but not necessarily curing. However, women have the opportunity to live well and die well. This new understanding emphasizes the importance of the patients' position as a pro-active participant in their own healing process.

Doctors, oncologists and natural therapists cannot switch on the "will to live" button for you. However by using effective language and their knowledge of the placebo effect, they can act as catalysts, fanning the embers of hope. Change can only come through personal awareness and it is up to the patient to take that role. However I also firmly believe that the health professional's role, whether it be conventional or complementary medicine, is to assist patients to take the first few steps on their road to recovery. Therapies and treatments have their place without doubt, but they are not substitutes for care, support and much needed attention to personal matters of the soul. The will to live is born out of a strong desire of not wanting to die and is a survival instinct that is often motivated by fear. In the process of healing, the experience of fear can be an active motivator in the short term.

However, the will to heal is quite a different experience. It is more motivated by belief in self, instinct and intuition and it is initiated by an inner awareness of the need for personal change and transformation. Not fear.

If fear is allayed and the above responses are activated the doorway to transformation can be opened. This is quite different from seeking the "magic bullet" and grasping desperately for "the cure". It is as if there is a bridge between the will to live (initially activated out of fear) and the will to heal (activated out of awareness). When you begin to cross the bridge between the two, you can begin to transform your life through the illness rather than passively lose your life to it.

The Practical Aspects of Breast Cancer

As well as dealing with the more intangible aspects we will also deal with the practical details of breast cancer management. We will be considering this from the point of view of your emotional healing. This will include some nutritional help, meditation/relaxation instruction, stress management, dealing with any side effects of treatments, and many facets of the care process. Issues relevant to hormones, osteoporosis and coping with surgically and chemically induced menopause will also be discussed. Knowledge and understanding of the recurrence of breast cancer and how to deal with it, will be of help to the many women who feel devoid of ideas, options and inspiration. After the recovery of my ex-husband in 1978 we assessed all that we had done to aid the remission process. From our experience the first support groups evolved. Given the large amount of research now available on the effects of support groups, there is a section discussing the various types of groups, from the simple structures to the more therapeutic models and their effectiveness.

The information and ideas contained in **Women of Silence** *is not intended to replace any medical care and treatment that you may be having. Rather my hope is that it will give you understanding and clarity regarding your individual situation. In doing that you will be better able to develop a healing programme that incorporates the best that orthodox medicine has to offer with the best of other complementary approaches. My wish is that you have embraced the best chance of not only surviving but thriving, flourishing and really living and so enjoying a better life through and beyond breast cancer.*

Overview

This Introduction is written with you in mind. If you are using this book for healing, the sections are clearly headed and designed so that small sections can be read easily and built upon throughout the book. It is important that younger women who are currently well, learn about their emotional self-care and its importance for their health. Using the stories of thousands of women and the wisdom drawn from them, is not new as a teaching tool. This was the way of indigenous cultures that did not write their stories but rather passed on the wisdom of the previous generations through word, image and drama. As well as building on generation history, these stories derive from thousands of women in current time and are relevant to the culture and times that we live in. This makes them very accessible as tools for developing awareness and providing following generations of women with a compass to help navigate their life's journey. Women who have experienced breast cancer have consistently said that *Women of Silence* should not merely be limited to educating women with breast cancer. Rather it should have a role as a resource for women in bringing attention to the care of their emotional health. Hence this new work should be valued for information about *prevention, management, healing and education* in women's health, as well as for breast cancer. Most women will invariably know someone in their sphere of friends that has breast cancer. Fear of breast cancer still seems a significant issue in the Western World despite campaigns to alleviate it. When the illness is understood and de-mystified, fear is dispelled.

In 1994 the publication of ***Women of Silence: The Emotional Healing of Breast Cancer*** brought public and professional awareness to the importance of the role of emotions in the healing of breast cancer. Also, it looked at how women in general, manage their emotional issues. In relation to breast cancer, now almost ten years later, supportive care is more available. Many hospitals are involved in piloting complementary medicine units; however gaps still exist in the delivery of services of supportive, complementary and alternative care. Healing has become a *busy-ness* of too many options, pills, diets, techniques and methods. All of which require large amounts of energy to be expended — energy that people with cancer do not possess.

During the past 20 years medical treatments and diagnostic techniques have certainly improved. In fact these innovations can now substantially extend life. However their effectiveness does not necessarily mean that there is a corresponding effect on life quality. Concurrently while mind–body medicine has expanded, little attention is being paid to the emotional and spiritual issues that are, in essence, the core of our lives. My approach has been to help women to heal the effects of chronic stress, become re-empowered, build resilience and re-engage their lost passion. It is from this foundation of strength that these other treatments and therapies have the best possible chance of success. When treatments of any kind are engaged, not through desperation or grasping at straws, but through well considered conscious choice, then, accordingly, the outcomes will be greatly improved.

Cause and Effect

I am very conscious, at the outset, to put to rest the common new age theory that you caused your illness. Unfortunately this now widely espoused belief has been counter-productive for many women and can be responsible for inducing guilt and feelings of personal inadequacy. The obvious progression being that if you know what caused your breast cancer you can fix it. It's not that simple! This elusive chase more often than not causes a great deal of grief and when the cause is not found and remedied, women feel a great sense of failure and loss of hope. In contrast *Women of Silence* looks at the associations of how you, as a person, have responded to life, your contact with others, your relationships, your boundaries and how your lost passion might be rekindled. At the time of diagnosis it is important not to beat yourself up over causes or to over-extend your already limited energy resources in the pursuit of the magic cure. Taking time is imperative. Pursue medical options and seek second or third opinions if you are unclear or uncomfortable.

I will emphasize the need for incorporating new stress management methods while suggesting ways of discharging the old habitual stress patterns, held in your body, sometimes for a lifetime. While concurrently using the illness as a point for re-empowerment in your life, you can build personal resilience on all levels: physical, psychological, emotional and spiritual. From this base of strength you can plan your strategy for recovery and healing.

Healing in "The Big Picture"

Dealing with life and all illness can be thought about on two levels. This is a simple model that can easily be understood. There is the "small picture view" and "the big picture view". Religion and spirituality form a sort of bridge between the two. I see the "small picture view" as the day-to-day; the daily habitual motions that we go through; the human *doing* rather than the human *being*. The "big picture" is more about our development as human beings. It is the mystical view, a view of the soul's journey in this life before we physically leave it. In relation to illness, if we can view the importance of treating the person as well as the illness, we are offering a reality of care that will, without doubt, impact on the person's quality of life and their life as a spiritual journey. It also will influence their death as a spiritual journey.

This is where I believe that adversity and illness can teach us much about life and death.

A journey seeking only the *cure* may be just a physical experience and begs the question, *"What tools has one learned to make life better?"* When the illness recurs or, as happens, changes into another form, then the questioning begins and illness becomes a spiritual issue allowing the journey of self-awakening to begin. A journey seeking healing should not be one of desperation or grasping and nor should it be motivated solely by the fear of dying.

If the journey does not take you down the path of questioning the meaning of life and the mystery of life and death, then I believe it has not served you well. For there is one thing for certain and that is, that one day we all will die. You can cheat and bargain with many things in life but you can't cheat death. Life and death dance closely together. Getting to know and be comfortable with them both means we are much freer to enjoy our existence.

If healing is only focused upon firing the right chemical or nuclear ammunition at clumps of cells, which pays no attention to a person's essence, soul or spirit, then it is shallow. I encourage you to explore the mystery.

A Brief History of My Ideas and Methods

Having inspired and pioneered an innovative cancer support service with my now ex-husband in 1981, I was fortunate to spend very personal time with many thousands of women with breast cancer over a period of some twenty two years. The introduction of residential programmes to this service in the mid-eighties allowed me to glean an even greater understanding of the issues surrounding breast cancer. This was due to the time able to be given to the content of the life stories told by women in the groups. In listening to their case histories, the message was clear and universal for women. The message about prevention, health promotion and living well is an obvious thread that will be discussed in the pages to come.

As a woman I have been touched deeply by the lives and stories of so many women affected by breast cancer. As a holistic healer, it would not be appropriate for me to maintain silence or withhold the knowledge and insights I have gained through their sharing. At this moment, as I write, I am thinking about all the women with breast cancer who have journeyed in and out of my life over the years; each one of them being like strong threads in the finely woven fabric of life. Some have survived with immense dignity and courage. Others have died with immense dignity and courage. They showed a remarkable ability to take charge of their lives and take charge of their death. It has been an honour to be in the company of such brave women.

Their life stories are such an inspiration that it is my hope that all women will be encouraged to read *Women of Silence*.

Breast cancer holds great fear for many women and the fact is that women are now being diagnosed in younger age groups with often quite aggressive tumours despite all the improved diagnostic efforts that are made. The information and insights I have written about have been drawn from working with more than 10,000 people affected by cancer. Are there lessons to learn from these exceptional lives? I think so. I encourage you to use this information as a springboard from which you can dive into life with renewed inspiration, energy and passion. Take a risk and make a sea change.

Make tomorrow the first day of the rest of your life!

Chapter One

Taking the Journey of Cancer

Stories can provide hope, inspire faith and show what is possible. The human spirit is awesome. Nurtured and tended, our spirit of survival can provide the background for healing and sometimes for curing. Here is a synopsis of the Gawler (my former married name) story as never before written. It is realistic, verifiable and shows the possibilities for anyone who has to deal with cancer. It demonstrates what is possible if we can keep the flame of hope and faith alive and the spirit of unconditional love, in action.

The key learning and wisdom from our story is highlighted in italics. I recommend that your carers and supporters read this chapter so that they might better understand the journey you are taking. Remember, if you have a supporting partner, then it is their journey too. One thing is guaranteed; you will not emerge from the experience as the same people. Change will always bring consequences. Many people's desire is to get back to where they were in life before the cancer was diagnosed. In my experience that never happens; for once this experience has touched you, you are never the same again.

For more than 27 years now, cancer has occupied a major part of my life. As with most people this uninvited, life-threatening group of aberrant cells called cancer, entered our lives without warning. But as with many of life's major events, we found that we had limited resources in knowing how to deal with it.

It was a memorable Christmas time in 1974 when my partner discovered a small lump in the middle of his right thigh. The

1

diagnosis: a rapidly growing tumour, named osteogenic sarcoma, and a relatively rare cancer to be seen in a twenty five year old. This cancer is renowned for its ability to reproduce bone cells at an alarming rate. It was extremely serious, and considering our age and limited life experience, we were relatively ill equipped to deal with it.

The changes in life that a diagnosis brings are rapid, and this was no exception.

Only eight days after diagnosis he had a full leg amputation on the eighth of January 1975. I lived with and cared for him throughout that year and, as we travelled around Australia, he took up painting but we made little change to our lifestyle. Medically, the tumour was very advanced and the prognosis was not at all good. With luck, they said, he might be one of the 5% alive in five years time.

We thought positively which, in retrospect, seemed more like denial. We were not proactive at all and just wished that the cancer would not return.

Late in 1975 a secondary bone cancer was diagnosed. We were faced with a grim prognosis of three to six months. At this time, with no medical treatment available to offer curative hope, we set out as pioneers on a healing journey with fire in our souls and passion in our hearts. We headed into uncharted waters making up our own map as we went along by gathering and assessing information. This was the beginning of a roller coaster ride of assorted therapies that ultimately led to a healing through most extraordinary circumstances.

We incorporated an intensive dietary regime. We tried the Gerson diet that, in the beginning, seemed to make a lot of sense. Indeed, a major part of our veterinary practice had been involved with high performance animals: racehorses, trotters and greyhounds that all required additional nutritional help — vitamins, minerals and trace elements. Their nutritional status was probably much better than that of

2

their owners! It seemed natural to us, therefore, that a health promoting diet could help in the healing process. I had been a vegetarian since the age of five and had practised a healthy lifestyle so that it was second nature to me. I was keen to participate. I made twelve fresh juices daily (on a hand juicer for the first two months) and helped with enemas, injections and supplements. I made bread and cheese and bought and grew organic vegetables. Eighteen hours of my day was occupied with food. On a very practical note, I also became the chauffeur so that he could attend all his various appointments as most of them were about one hour's drive away from where we were living. As well as the diet, this became a very stressful healing programme.

Being proactive and using food as my healing tool gave me a focus during the difficult times but, in retrospect, the diet was far too stringent. So much so that we forgot about enjoying life!

At the same time Ian began to make the connection between his cancer and his own life and particularly his stress levels. Against a background of unresolved grief and other significant life issues, he began the path of self-exploration. He had indeed been living life in the fast lane, regularly working eighty hours each week; training and competing in the decathlon; playing in the local football team and leading an active social life with "yours truly". Life was fast and fun; but insidiously stressful.

Concurrently meditation also entered our healing programme. I knew little about it and was sceptical; but he was keen. Ian attended a six-week course with Dr Ainslie Meares, a Melbourne psychiatrist who had an intense interest in hypnosis and a type of meditation he called *mental ataraxis*. This was a technique of "totally letting go" — that is, without the use of one's willpower and **striving** or **trying** to achieve a state of calm or stillness — very hard to do when your life may depend upon it! This type of meditation could lead to a deep inner stillness and Meares believed that massive stress

3

reduction and management through intensive meditation could lead to remission from cancer. Ian enjoyed these sessions immensely and also enjoyed meeting fellow cancer patients — all on the path of self-discovery. In fact outside of the meditation room there was much interaction and sharing of therapies and ideas by the attending patients. They formed their own breakaway support group — perhaps to balance out the long silences required by the Meare's technique. They established strong bonds that must have added some type of therapeutic effect. For Ian however, being in intense and unrelenting pain with the secondary cancer, it was always an issue and he would often spend up to five hours per day trying to meditate effectively and relax. Meditation gave him a focus and built hope in the absence of any other recommended treatments. However at that time, meditation proved to be lacking in effective pain management and for the supporting partner it was very challenging. The meditation sessions with Meares were only two to three hours and that left the remaining twenty one hours of the day to get through until the next day. Another complication was the distance and time involved in travel. The journeys were sometimes gruelling.

Dealing with chronic and unrelenting pain is exhausting for all concerned. It seemed that there was so much to get to know quickly about symptoms that demanded immediate action.

I began meditation as a support and, although I had been sceptical at first, the theory made sense to me and I soon felt some benefit. But it was easy for me. I could play with it, as my life wasn't on the line. But I also felt that meditation did not hold all the answers for a cure; but it was useful to assist with self reflection and re-evaluation of one's life. I had known then (and since) of many women, including Buddhist nuns, who were meditators and vegetarians and yet they succumbed to breast and bowel cancers; there had to be something more! Ian struggled on through much frustration and increasing pain levels. Eventually the pain demanded so much of our attention that it became the *dis-ease* and meditation became almost impossible. It seems that prior knowledge and experience of these methods is a distinct advantage rather than having to learn them in the midst of an illness; a daunting and difficult task. For some reason it seemed easier while he was in Meares' office to achieve some respite; but away from him and the group it was so much harder. It seemed, at times, that there was so much to change and learn that it was overwhelming. During these very stressful times people tend to try so hard to heal and change so many things in their pursuit of healing.

Leaving the familiar and safe behind you and changing your lifestyle can be very stressful, especially if you believe that your survival depends upon getting it right.

It is important to remember to be gentle with yourself!

Everyone needs a supporter on the ground and for a time this became the role for my friend Pat Coleby. Pat saw me through some dark and difficult times. She knew at heart what we were up against as she had been through the cancer experience with her son. I remain grateful that she was always there for me when I needed someone to talk with, especially during the times when Ian, the patient, was silent.

Cancer, as we all know, can be an isolating disease for the patient but unless you have been through it, you may not appreciate that being the supporting partner can be a lonely path too. I discovered that this path can be made even more isolating because I believed against all the medical odds that the person I was supporting could and would get well. A radiotherapist at the time curtly gave me his best advice which was: "*Stop chasing rainbows and just accept that Ian is going to die!*".

However amongst much scepticism and at times, aggressive opposition, and after three months of the meditation and dietary approach, tumours that had been previously growing at an alarming rate defied all predictions. They barely increased in size! It was at this point, however, that we experienced a major setback when a dramatic increase in pain and other alarming symptoms saw us returning to the medical model searching for solutions. At this point we ceased the sessions with Ainslie Meares as he could offer us no other solution for dealing with the pain. We went on to develop our own style of meditation. Things were deteriorating. An enlarged inguinal lymph node that had become a bony secondary tumour, resulted in an obstructed ureter and a severe kidney problem developed. Palliative radiotherapy proved ineffective for the pain and we were fast running out of options.

An injection of a natural mistletoe extract brought some relief for back pain as did acupuncture. There were more than the cancer issues to be dealt with, as is so often the case. Symptoms more associated with the strains of living life on one leg and a rapid weight loss, through a too stringent diet, were all too evident and starting to take their toll. Our cross to bear became the insidious pitfall of …

getting more stressed while trying to de-stress.

At this point and despite all the setbacks and the pain, I accepted a proposal of marriage given in the back of the car after a radiotherapy session! Medically it was expected that he would live only for a few weeks, but I still had other ideas! Somehow I was able to maintain a dauntless faith of working through the illness. Whether it was denial, proactive thinking, my belief system, intuition or sunspots, I really can't say. I only know that whatever it was that drove me (and still does), I do not have the tendency to give up! Ian as the patient was having his own experience and for whatever reasons, we both focused our energies on solutions and possibility thinking.

In March of 1976 (unbelievably) we found ourselves on a plane bound for Manila and Baguio City in the Philippines. My charge was now six and a half stone in weight, jaundiced, in severe pain and now a tumour had spread to the left lung. We stayed for one month and visited five healers but, unhappily, there was little change in the tumours — in fact they grew a little. However, psychologically and spiritually there had been a shift. In fact during the month that we stayed he gained eight kilograms (seventeen pounds) in weight, the pain became negligible and he was still alive!

The significant difference was that when we left the Philippines Ian had become a person "living" with cancer. When we left Australia earlier all the symptoms showed that, even with some minute optimism, he was a person dying from cancer.

This is an important choice point or crossroad on the healing journey and one that many people have experienced. It doesn't have to be the Philippines that is the catalyst; it could be any activity, practise, healer or event that can potentially switch on your life force again.

One important factor in our experience was the friendship and ongoing mentorship of an Australian healer, Norma. She had befriended me during a visit to the first healer and was very instrumental in the whole process of recovery. She became a spiritual adviser to us both for many years and she became my mentor. When we met in the Philippines she had asked me if I was a healer and I replied that I was just here with a sick person. I remember she looked at me for a very long time. One of those timeless times! She possessed deep, searching, enormous pale blue eyes, framed by snowy, silver hair and a presence that one doesn't easily forget. She asked me to her home on the next Sunday but left without telling me where she lived and Baguio is a large town. I was determined to meet her again so that Sunday, unbelievably, and after providing many descriptions of her appearance to local Filipinas, we eventually found her home and spent a day that was to change the rest of my life. She introduced me to magnetic healing (similar to the later introduced Reiki and Therapeutic Touch methods) which proved to be the most single helpful practise we engaged in. Ian found this so beneficial that I worked on him for five hours each and every day for the first three months after our return; then three hours daily. During the years ahead a one-hour session was a part of the daily routine, long after he had recovered. I had boundless energy in those days. I have no doubt that the effect of focused and loving touch, given with intention and received with openness, over such a long period of time was a major contribution to restoring his health. Personally I believe that the combination of touch and deep relaxation was a profound one.

We applied whatever we felt would help Ian's situation and, in fact, we used thirty-one different therapeutic approaches during the time of the illness. These included experimental chemotherapy, visits to other healers as well as travelling to India to see Holy Man, Sathya Sai Baba. We encountered many highs and lows throughout the entire journey. It was hard work and our mettle and perseverance were continually put to the test. However with commitment and zeal we actively continued throughout the years ahead with our mainstay approaches of nutrition, meditation and magnetic healing.

Thus Ian became a person not only living with cancer, but now living very well with cancer.

Unknowingly at that time we were pioneering a supportive and integrated care approach; part of a wave of cancer approaches that were happening independently in many places around the world.

Two and a half years after we had begun this journey, in July 1978, he was declared cancer free. But the story has an amazing twist. What was responsible for the remission? The bony tumours had been shrinking over a period of several months prior to this and, as well, Ian had been coughing up small amounts of bone and quite a lot of blood. By June of 1978 all the visible tumours had disappeared; but what remained was a productive cough and sore swollen joints that demanded a medical opinion. We received the good news and the bad news on June 30. The cancer was gone; but Ian had active TB! It had been evident on X-ray for more than two years but all the cancer specialists had missed it! It appears that the TB may have been an important part of the healing process. Two diseases vying for habitation in the one host! There is a volume of research on the connections between TB bacilli and remission from bone cancer. Particularly interesting is the work of Dr William Coley of Coley's toxins fame.

The key issue of interest to me is that had we given up and just believed the expected outcomes, then the two-week prognosis of 1976 would have become a reality. He would not have survived long enough to have the TB assist in the healing in the way it did. The message from our story is this: If you live each day with cancer and live for the day, then the days multiply until one day you find that you are living well with cancer; after that the possibilities are endless. One never knows what it will be that completes the healing or the curing — be it medical or complementary or alternative or spiritual or all of them!

I was pregnant and overdue with our first daughter the day of the TB diagnosis. The news must have jolted me into labour for the next day our first born arrived; but of course he could not be present at the birth. Instead he delivered me to the front of a small hospital in Blackwood, South Australia. I delivered Rosemary and he delivered himself for an enforced stay at a sanatorium!

It had been a lengthy but rewarding journey back to health for us both. I too had lived through an extraordinary experience, having been a supporting partner to a cancer patient who journeyed to the edge of life and who survived and thrived. The arrival of our daughter was a highpoint as well. We had been told that, due to the treatments, there was little possibility of us having children.

In 1981, based on our experience, we began actively working with other cancer patients and their carers and, as a result, founded Australia's first self-help cancer support group which evolved into an internationally acclaimed centre for cancer support.

Some Key Points from this Story

This was our journey. Don't try to replicate it. Keep in mind your journey will be different. It is tempting to follow the regimes of others; but there is no one-size-fits-all in healing! Rather look at the key elements written in italics. In learning to trust yourself, your instincts, your intuitions, re-finding your empowerment, and living your truth and passion (and if you've lost them taking the time to discover what they are) you will find that doors open and synchronicities happen. The key point is choosing life whatever the prognosis, keeping it simple and not taking away all of the familiar in the name of change and healing.

Remember too, that this story demonstrates the possibilities. Importantly too, this is the story of a *man* who had cancer and who had an energetic and supportive woman to do for him. I know many women who, even if partners are supportive, do not have that luxury of time and energy while the bills need to be paid and the children need to be cared for. Be sensible and set reasonable goals for yourselves. Many cancer patients tried to repeat the Gawler approach particularly after *Can You Conquer Cancer* was published in 1984. Although this inspiring book contains some terrific information, it is important for the cancer patient or partner seeking help, that it is read with the understanding that the book was written by, and from, a patient's point of view. Carers would have written it from a different perspective as they are the ones usually involved in the "doing" and the "helping". Both views are valid and useful in combination. Some good advice is to keep things in balance and remember the old adage: *all things in moderation*!

All that being said please keep hope, faith and love alive and active in your life. Once you have made the conscious choice to live with breast cancer, then live **well** with breast cancer

10

and then one never knows what opportunities will present for either healing or curing!

Physician Heal Thyself — My Experience as the Patient

Working with large groups of people affected by cancer has been a unique opportunity and a profound learning experience. It has helped me to keep walking my talk, practising what I preach and living my truth.

Over the years I have gained many qualifications in a variety of healthcare professions. But my most important and valuable learning, which completes the trilogy of experience as carer and health professional, has been to walk in the shoes of the patient.

We all have a vulnerable point and mine has been in the area of personal relationships. My marriage that began in the stormy waters of dealing with cancer in 1976 ended abruptly in November 1997. Uninvited change had again entered my life and its consequence was a deep personal grief and chaos for which I have not yet found words of description. The responsibility for a Foundation and all that was involved in the integrity of its operation had taken its toll on us. We had lost our way.

Suffice to say here that, within days of the separation, a major medical crisis ensued. The condition left me with a paralysed rectum and lower bowel. Now my own life story was playing out a similar scenario to that of the many patients I had worked with. With no support, limited finance, a huge mortgage, a farm and twelve horses to manage and with three young teenagers my familiar life came crashing down around me. I still marvel that uninvited change has been so attracted to my life; but I remind myself of Ilana's words of wisdom: "Bad things do happen to good people and be careful not to normalise the abnormal too much or you forget what is normal!" So my journey as a patient began under very

11

difficult personal circumstances. I have had the opportunity to have my mettle well and truly tested and I am still here to tell the story!

With this acquired condition, all of the issues that surround breast cancer also became daily issues for me to deal with: Treatments, surgeries, highly invasive diagnostic tests, altered body image and sexuality, riding the medical rollercoaster, bowel obstructions, ileostomies, colostomies and a life-altering condition. But how lucky I was, I had learned so much from my patients and, combined with my resilience, determination and perseverance, I eventually found my solution. After six years, with a large portion of my large colon removed, bagless and wiser, the re-write of *Women of Silence* is the result. Walking in the shoes of the patient has added a depth of understanding and compassion which has well and truly rekindled my desire to seize my own life again in the service of myself and others. I have learned at a very personal level about the energetic power of emotions; that is, when they flow too much or that they are withheld for too long, then their powerful effects will manifest somewhere in the body.

While I regard each patient as an individual and have a dislike for rash generalizations, experience has shown that there has been no avoiding the powerful emergence of common issues and traits among people with cancer. This applies particularly when we consider women with breast cancer as a group.

Prolonged and unresolved stress seemed to be an obvious life pattern in these women. Coupled with this, there is usually a major change in life circumstances that appears to act as the trigger mechanism for the onset of ill health. In my observation not only cancer, but other *dis-eases* such as Chronic Fatigue Syndrome, Lupus and Irritable Bowel Syndrome (to name but a few) can relate to this same pattern. Maybe our behavioural type, genetics and environment dictate the why and how. Most breast cancer patients can identify the time when they knew something was not right with their health. They can also identify the time, long before, when they felt the effects of a trauma of some kind and never felt the same again.

If one takes the time to listen to the life story of a woman with breast cancer, rather than just concentrating on what is medically wrong with them, a whole new arena opens up in understanding the nature of the illness. On a time basis it would be very difficult to do this individually and this is where group work excels. In an atmosphere of support and safety and with the common bond of illness as the carte blanche for sharing and expression, the stories of how people have lived and coped with their lives are both moving and telling.

For women with breast cancer, an effective support group can be a vital link in the progression from stifled silence towards a life of ease, where open communication can more readily be expressed and shared. Identifying these patterns, stresses and emotional issues leads to the recognition of the need to encourage more community and social support in the area of illness. Further, this applies directly to the prevention of *disease*, its management and the promotion of healthy lifestyles throughout the community.

It is in the spirit of sharing the experiences and learning of others, that this book is offered.

Why was *"Women of Silence"* Written?

Women with breast cancer often appear to have developed a way of coping that involves the "bottling up" or the withholding of some kind of emotional energy. Usually this emotional energy centres around painful experiences which these women have felt incapable of resolving effectively. So, silence instead of expression. This silence is an in-built method of embalming a woman's wounds for the obvious reasons of immediate survival and life preservation. Often "withholding" is the only means of maintaining oneself

13

through a crisis. But at some point there needs to be a discharge, a letting go of the event or events; otherwise the memory will linger on in both the mind and the body. This can lead to an insidious and subtle ill-at-ease which, if unattended, builds up, crisis after crisis, year after year.

Often women have reported to me that this contained emotional energy seems to have quite a specific feeling and a place where it is stored within their being. They described this feeling as a void. This void feels like hollowness — an unresolved emptiness. It is a feeling — a space that contains the sense of what is missing and unfulfilled in their life. This feeling of emptiness has a physical location. Asked where it is, most women with breast cancer almost wistfully, invariably gently, tenderly, touch the area over the middle of their chest, or a little lower over their solar plexus.

Most women with breast cancer with whom I have discussed this, immediately recognise this place, the place of the void. Just as quickly, they will say it had been so hard to talk of it, to describe it or to share it with anyone else. For many of these women this place had an almost fourth dimensional quality. It went with a feeling of being removed from their customary sense of reality, a feeling of being somehow outside of themselves; like a portion of them existed in another dimension — this "fourth" dimension. This is a classic response to trauma known as disassociation and is a part of the now recognised PTSD (Post Traumatic Stress Disorder). Women identify it but don't know what to do about it. Health professionals often do not attend to it and, if they do recognise it, they also often don't know what to do about it.

Another term I use for this is the inner vessel of the feminine. For this is a place where women can seal their silence and seal their pain. With this vessel sealed and the pain contained, coping becomes possible; life can go on — at least on the surface. But the "void" remains on the inside.

This inner pain and its containment is a feeling common to many women. Having their experience devalued, or not even recognised or acknowledged, can add to personal frustration and lead to inner suffering. It is this suffering which in turn leads further into the "void".

For many men this will come as useful information. I believe that many males have quite a different experience and it is my observation, from personal and clinical experience, that very few men come to know how it is for women. Perhaps this relates to what I notice in many men. It seems that their mode of feeling may have a different mechanism of expression compared with many women's modes of feeling. For men, their feeling mode often involves a sense of a deep inner grief. When this inner grief is denied expression, as it often is, it results in a sense of "numbness" to life. This has been described to me many times by men as a feeling of containment or freezing rather than a feeling of a void. This numbness or containment dulls the pain allowing men to "soldier on". Again it may be a useful survival mechanism, and life may go on, yet if their feelings are numb then these can limit or even block their ability to feel what their partner might be going through. A diagnosis of breast cancer can really test a relationship. If there are problems in a relationship pre-diagnosis, there will most likely be problems post-diagnosis. The illness can provide an opportunity for a profound healing if a relationship is open to it and a couple possess the desire to re-state their love for each other.

Although men may be supportive in many ways, and usually this is done by doing and filling practical roles, a woman may find that to share her feelings and to have those feelings understood at a gut level may be too much to ask for, or even expect. The inability of couples to share feelings can become a frustration that can make for very dramatic dynamics between men and their women who are going through breast cancer. Hopefully, reading this book will give men a direct insight into more of what it is to be a woman with breast cancer; and hopefully, enable them to provide a more caring and effective support for their women.

Another key and challenging issue in my work with women with breast cancer has been the observation that a majority of them *appear* to be calm and passive people in terms of their personality type. But beneath this layer of coping, I have often found that their calmness masks the "void" and that their silence is one of despair and a feeling of hopelessness. Emotions of repressed anger, resentment, unhappiness and discontent are veiled by a *passive* silence. This silence will produce major hurt and it is also my experience that women with breast cancer can identify readily with this description of silence.

Yet, happily, there is another type and quality of silence. Importantly this other sacred silence holds the possibility to heal us.

For there is a creative silence, a nourishing silence, that is the silence of inner peace, the silence of quiet contentment, self-assuredness, limitless potential and joyful expression.

In my view, drawn from my experience, real healing can only take place when there is a *conscious* transition from the state of "bottled up" emotionally distressed silence, to the state of open communication and expression. This transforms to the state of inner nourishing silence and its product — *PEACE OF MIND*.

I believe that good communication and expression are essential for bringing about the processes that lead towards healing. When we carry too much emotional baggage it is very difficult to experience true peace of mind. However, if expression can be activated along with the will to live and the will to heal, then the process of meditation can then be practiced and developed to bring a very deep and profound experience of this inner nourishing silence. This type of silence can well be described as the silence of sacred solitude. It is in these quiet moments of sacred silence, when we experience the stillness of meditation in the gap between thoughts, that we are given a glimpse of the possibilities. In that space we have the opportunity to experience our truth — who we really are!

This is where emotional healing is to be found. This experience is like a journey; a journey which offers the very real prospect of being able to live life fully; to realise our goals and to evolve through and beyond the cancer experience.

Such a journey is unique for each woman. Although the *physical disease* may seem similar in all women, due to different life circumstances, every woman's path to recovery will be uniquely hers.

My hope is that the experience of other women who have travelled this path and who have shared their stories with me will, combined with my own insight and experiences, help more women to journey, with peace and confidence, to a land of better health.

Chapter Two

Discovering the "Wounds"

Women of Silence

Women of Silence, gentle and strong,
Tell me your path, where it first went wrong.
Tell me your story, how you've coped with your life.
Tell me about all the trouble and the strife.

I see how you've coped withholding the pain,
I feel your soul weeping and yet you refrain
From sharing your losses, your grief and your fears
But you know, they multiply over the years.

Until one day your inner wisdom says "no more".
And you awake with an illness, a fiery core
That's fuelled by a lifestyle out of control,
Too much held too often has taken its toll.

It's time to rethink, reassess how it's been
And develop a strategy previously unseen.
There is a way to heal with heart and great passion.
Let go of withholding that was always your fashion.

Nurture yourself and make yourself whole.
Live your life fully and realise your goals.
Women of Silence, gentle and strong,
Find the courage to heal, and to sing your heart's song.

Grace Adamson.

A Formula for Discovery and Transformation

The poem *Women of Silence*, written in 1994, is a distillation of story content as told to me by my patients. A few years after writing the poem I met Basque storyteller and healer Angeles Arrien. Through her studies of cross-cultural societies she had also distilled into words the essence of discovering the "wound". If you have chosen to walk the path of self-discovery my suggestion is that you read the poem and then ask yourself the four questions listed below. The questions appear simple but you may be surprised at the depth of your discovery. Writing the answers in a journal will be a very helpful tool to bring awareness to the core issues of your life that are in need of healing.

Almost a blueprint of my poem, these questions can provide the foundation for your personal development plan. They formulate the discovery into four basic life questions. If you visited a healer, a shaman or a medicine man with the intent of recovery from an illness or condition, they would ask you four questions. It goes like this … they would ask:

1. *Where in your life did you stop singing?*
2. *Where in your life did you stop dancing?*
3. *Where in your life did you become disenchanted with story; particularly the sound of your own life story?*
4. *Where in your life did you notice you became uncomfortable with silence, especially the sound of your own inner sacred silence?*

The answers to these questions are to do with "soul loss" which encompass all healing that is outside the medical framework.

The Wound and Breast Cancer

From the earliest days of working with women with breast cancer I noticed a common thread — so many of these women told stories of extraordinary life experiences. Commonly, they had faced many traumas and hurdles in their lives, yet somehow they managed to adopt coping skills that enabled them to push on and survive. They all displayed a character of great inner strength born of prolonged coping. However, commonly, this coping mechanism had become unstuck. It seemed for so many that within their history a life-changing event, an event of insurmountable magnitude, had occurred eighteen months to two years prior to diagnosis. This seemed to be the proverbial "straw that broke the camel's back" as this event invariably targeted the one vulnerable area in a woman who appeared to be resilient and coping. For other women, experiencing chronic stress had formed the background of their lives. At some point just one load too many came along and they switched off from life, becoming automatic responders to the demands of others.

Trauma, prior to diagnosis, adds to the trauma of diagnosis which, in turn, adds to post diagnosis trauma. For many this multi layered affect of trauma, left unattended, can create a snowball effect resulting in poor response to treatments, medical and otherwise, and a reduced quality of life. Some studies have also suggested that quantity of life may be affected also. What happens at the level of brain chemistry during this process now gives a demonstrable effect on the body and the immune system. This science called PNI (psycho-neuro-immunology) can demonstrate both the biochemical effects of trauma on the body as well as the biochemical effects of therapeutic solutions that a woman may choose. In other words healing of this nature is now demonstrable.

The life issues that women with breast cancer have described, are universal — running the full gamut of human experiences. They include divorce, grief, miscarriages, stillbirths, abortions, redundancy, betrayal, bankruptcy and other similar significant issues. These are not the "small change" events of life as they seem to have an ability to shock the individual woman to her very marrow. It seems that the vulnerability of women who develop breast cancer lies in the way they attempt to cope with major emotional trauma. In this scenario the issue is either silenced or not given an opportunity to be voiced, grieved or dealt with. It is not uncommon for people to just get on with life and try to leave these things behind; but that solution is not an ideal one. The wounds of the psyche are just as severe as the physical wounds of the body. It is just that we don't see the blood; instead we bleed energetically, become fatigued and ill.

We now know that the brain and the body have an intricate system of communication right down to the tiniest molecules. Cells have memory too and many traumas of life that can be denied existence by the mind, are recorded somewhere in the body such as in the muscle cells, the immune system and so on. The body tissue can store frozen trauma and other emotional material. Real and lasting healing is the thaw. Our genetic propensity and conditioning is also likely to play a role in these mechanisms. Touch is one of the key methods that can communicate on all the levels of body, mind, emotion and spirit. Touch can help the thawing out process. Needless to say the touch must be safe, invited and given by a trusted therapist, healer or caring and loving partner.

The work of Ilana Rubenfeld, considered the grand dame of somatic psychotherapy in the USA, combines talk therapy with touch therapy, a method known as *RSM — Rubenfeld Synergy Method*. This elegant method has effectively demonstrated the healing potency of working with the memory of trauma in the body as well as in the mind, emotion and spirit. I have been blessed to study with her and found that our understanding of emotions from our different experiential backgrounds concurred completely.

The Survivor Personality — Diagnosis, Prognosis and Beyond

It was noticeable in our support groups, that when people spoke of their lives and their cancers, other patients in the room would begin to nod knowingly as they identified how their own story aligned with those dealing with the same cancer.

We all have an ability to switch off our life force and lose our passion for living. When we do so there is a message given to the soul and we die. This ability has also been demonstrated in many indigenous cultures including the Australian Aborigine, the Kikuyu of Kenya and the Bushmen of the Kalahari. There have been many instances of this phenomenon. These cultures live very much in the here and now, so when imprisoned they believe it is forever and they simply die. They lose their will to live. The Australian Aborigine is well known for the phenomenon of "bone pointing" which is discussed in more detail in another section of this book.

There are parallels between these experiences and the experiences of those diagnosed with a life-threatening illness. Often, much depends on how the diagnosis and prognosis were delivered to the patient. At a vulnerable moment, information poorly delivered by a doctor and/or poorly received by the patient can cause the spirit to retreat and withdraw, eventually resulting in death. I have known many patients with six months to live who die almost to the day as if set by some invisible internal clock. When lack of hope and possibility are vocalised by a person of power, the patient is, at that moment, faced with a life and death decision. So powerful can it be, that all else, all survival messages, are filtered out of awareness and death begins its course.

Bad news delivered well gives hope and a survival message. Bad news delivered without hope, equals a patient that dies on schedule.

The survivor message can be encouraged by re-empowering yourself and learning how to take control of your life. The strength that ultimately harmed you could be converted into a different strength that could heal you.

Two streams of understanding developed throughout the early years of our support groups. There were common denominators in personality types that emerged and often the participants would automatically bond with others in the group not knowing that they had a similar cancer to their own. Also they were quick to develop great camaraderie and identification with each other. Combining this with similarities in their personality types made for some interesting anecdotal research and alerted me to the existence of *the survivor personality*. As we worked with large numbers of people in our groups it enabled us to view a large cross section of the cancer population. It became apparent to me that the type of people we were dealing with all possessed strong personalities. Listening to their life stories they had, during the course of their lives, endured several stressful episodes as far back as early childhood. Maybe they were survivors who had just over-survived. Maybe they had coped just once too often. For some reason, usually an uninvited life crisis, they had lost their spirit or passion for life and succumbed to an illness. My herbal medicine teacher Dorothy Hall, used to describe cancer as the result of a series of lost battles in a person's life. The final lost battle being "the straw to break the camel's back".

The survivor message can be encouraged by re-empowering yourself and by learning how to take control of your life. The strength that ultimately harmed you could be converted into a different strength that could heal you. For example, women with breast cancer were frequently dealing with relationship issues, nurturing, shock and trauma; the bowel cancer patients often recognised a combination of diet, prolonged stress and usually a key unresolved emotionally distressing issue. I emphasise again that this is about awareness of how one has responded to life and is not about blame or self cause. Cancer is caused by many factors over a period of time. However the trigger factor, the overload factor, may be the final assault on the body's cancer defenses (the immune system).

The following stories serve to illustrate the differences in how people experience cancer.

Virginia was a woman dealing with primary breast cancer. After a lumpectomy and partial reconstruction she sought the services of a cancer support group. Within the group, Virginia felt safe enough to share the significant events in her life in recent years. She felt instinctively that these unresolved issues had something to do with her cancer situation and that dealing with it could only help her. I have been amazed by the number of women, like Virginia, who of their own volition, volunteer the connection between what has been going on in their lives and the status of their illness. They often volunteer in either an embarrassed or matter of fact manner, that they did not bother mentioning anything about their personal problems to their doctor, partners or friends for reasons of fear of ridicule or because of the risk of being ignored.

Virginia's life story had a huge impact on the group and there was not a dry eye in the house when she had finished. After having had great difficulty conceiving a child, Virginia became pregnant and miscarried at four months. This traumatic episode occurred twice more! The grief of these experiences was more than she could bear, resulting in her becoming very withdrawn from friends and life in general. She had just discovered that she was pregnant again prior to the diagnosis of her breast lump. As chemotherapy was recommended, and pregnancy viewed as dangerous for a woman with breast cancer, the pregnancy was terminated. Also, Virginia was told that it would be likely that the treatment would render future pregnancies impossible. This was an emotionally traumatic issue for this woman. I asked her what had happened to the bodies of the tiny miscarried fetuses? Was she allowed to see them and be with them, had she been able to grieve her loss? She thoughtfully and tearfully answered no. To make matters worse she had strong memories of the first miscarriage and the attending doctor saying to the nurse: "Take *that* away to pathology". *That* was her child! She became aware right at that very moment of how and when she had lost her spirit. Feeling a failure she not only withdrew from life but from herself. In the process of healing I recommended that she buy a rose bush as a symbol of each child's life and that she write a note to each child about how she felt then and now. She should buy the plants and wait until the right time to have her healing ritual and then bury a note under each rose. She could tend and nurture each rose. Every year the roses would grow and bloom and she could tend and nurture them in memory of those souls. The power of ritual in healing for women is phenomenal. Healing of this nature defies words and so the realm of image, symbol and ritual becomes the fertile ground for healthy grieving and recovery. Stories like this are not uncommon in women dealing with breast cancer.

The story of George on the other hand is from the male perspective and highlights the issues in his life. A man of European origin, George had come to Australia and settled with his wife in a small country town where they successfully developed a small business. They led a very stressful life, and, as a consequence, his wife Gerta developed chronically high blood pressure and heart problems. Gerta had to retire from the business, leaving George with massive amounts of work to cope with on his own. Realising the workload was beyond his capabilities, George hired a partner who ultimately betrayed his confidence, resulting in the business being declared insolvent. Shortly after, George had a car accident that placed even more pressure on an already overloaded financial situation. George developed cancer of the sigmoid colon within one year and at the time of diagnosis small secondary tumours were found in his liver. Surgery removed the bowel tumour but the liver secondaries were not operable. With new information from the cancer support group on board, George and Gerta began their healing journey. Together they began to learn about relaxation and stress management and about the role of nutrition in health. The latter turned out to be the most difficult for George who had left his homeland to live a life that could buy all the wonderful refined foods that were a part of the western lifestyle! He was highly unimpressed with being asked to go back to the unrefined diet of a Polish peasant!

The third example is that of a man called David, a school principal who developed a brain tumour. He regularly worked eighty hours each week, as well as pursuing a myriad of hobbies. A family man at heart, he recognized, after his diagnosis, that his life had been spinning out of control, he was not living as he wanted to live and he felt powerless to change it. Sailing was his favourite pastime but he became so busy that his yacht sat idly in his back yard waiting for a sailor who never arrived. Eventually David's wife moved out with the children to start a life of their own for, as husband and wife, the two of them had become "ships occasionally passing in the night". They subsequently divorced. This led to a total separation from his children due to the distance they had moved away. That resulted in him driving even harder into what he described as a workaholic frenzy. Eighteen months after the divorce David had a total breakdown and was found to have a large tumour in his brain. He now had an excuse to stop the merry-go-round and get off. He left work and read as much as he could about what options he had available for recovery. The prognosis was not good. Surgery was not recommended and he refused any other treatment. He now faced life differently, using his illness as an opportunity for change and with an understanding that made him feel reconnected to the magic he had lost. He learned to meditate, to manage his daily stress and began to eat a nutrient dense diet. His life assessment, brought on by his diagnosis, led him into dealing with many personal, emotional and psycho-spiritual issues. David survives today, maintaining good health, despite having been given a two-year prognosis twenty-five years ago! He has happily re-married, works from home and has maintained an exceptional *joie de vivre*.

Inevitably, cancer patients will have a story to tell that is worth listening to and there is much to be learned from this. Understandably your medical service providers do not have time to listen to your life story, so you need to explore other resources such as groups, one-to-one counselling and communicating with a partner in order to give voice to your story. A client who was dealing with chronic allergies recently wrote the following after finding her voice: "Things seem to be linking together. I am much happier about the past and have a better relationship with my husband and my son since I learned to *talk*. The raw anger that was hidden for so long (has) evaporated."

Change and be Who You Really Are?

Change, for some, is viewed as unfamiliar territory rather than a potential that lives within us — all the time. This is one of the valuable lessons I have learned from women with breast cancer. Understanding your strengths provides you with empowerment to translate one type of strength into another. This is how the strength that women had used to withhold emotional energy and which is often a part of the pattern of their disease, can be reframed; then transformed into strengths which have enormous healing potential.With the inner strength these women developed as they struggled to withhold emotional trauma, there came a related passivity. This passivity appeared to mask the inner turmoil that was felt at many times but not expressed. However, I discovered that many of the women with breast cancer that I was listening to, were not passive people by nature, but rather had adopted passiveness as a defence mechanism in order to survive. These women often came to say that the passive silence was developed with a view to keeping the peace. Using this strategy women become more compliant to the wishes of those around them and this was usually demonstrated by their lack of ability to say **NO**! These women, operating under great emotional pressure in their attempts to survive, learned to become "silent copers".

Joyce's Story — Learning to Say No

"Cancer has been my teacher and I have been a slow learner. But what I have learnt is that there is so much help out there to tap into if your are prepared to reach out. Simply try each path that opens up to you until you find the right one for you, that is, the ones that touch you deeply.

I had the first malignant carcinoma in my right breast. After a radical mastectomy my lymph glands were clear and it had been analysed as a primary cancer. My surgeon felt he had "got it all" and the prognosis was very good indeed. I recovered well and got back into the "busy-ness" of life again, feeling I had been "lucky". Exactly two years later I had visited my surgeon for a check-up and he was surprised to find another lump in the remaining breast. He arranged a mammogram and an ultrasound there and then. As he had just had a patient cancel an operation the following morning, he offered to slot me into that time if I would like to take it. So after a phone call to my husband I proceeded straight to the hospital. My husband was shocked, duly arrived and agreed it was better to get it over without delay.

My surgeon followed the same procedure as the first time; that is, removing the lump and having pathology (done) on it whilst I was anaesthetised, and as it was malignant, removing the whole breast and lymph glands. It was another primary cancer and oestrogen positive, whereas the first one was progesterone positive, but again my lymph glands were clear and so I felt incredibly "lucky" as he had "got it all". My surgeon and I both said "it can't happen again!" It was true enough, with the loss of both breasts and very much a Pollyanna attitude.

I decided, as I went to acquire my second prosthesis, that I could now be flexible and I chose to come down a size in bust measurement. It took me longer to recover the second time and I had to have my large keloid scar cut and redone as it was painful and kept waking me up at night. I had six radiation treatments to slow down the healing of the scar and I eventually started to feel comfortable once more.

Then three years later my world fell apart and I was shattered by the result of my bone scan that I had because of pain in my left ribs. The original pain was a red herring and not related to bone cancer but it fortunately enabled early detection of the twelve secondary tumours peppered through my bones in the neck, spine, clavicle, arm, ribs, hips and leg. The medical treatment prescribed was Nolvadex-D (Tamoxifen), a hormonal treatment taken orally.

I must say at this point that I consider myself fortunate in having the wonderful doctors I have. My wonderful GP over twenty years helped me with acupuncture and encouragement. My surgeon of fifteen years, whom I have utmost faith in, helped and encouraged me. So, knowing I had the best medical help available, I knew that I must reach out and tap into the best of self-help programmes that spoke to me. We attended a residential programme for cancer patients and their partners where we were taught many self-help methods to assist in my recovery. What an experience and journey lay ahead. I had no idea it could be so rewarding, fulfilling and exciting. At that point I decided that I was a very inhospitable host to this cancer invading my body and life and as I was rapidly running out of options, decided to give it my undivided attention.

I then had my scan months later and it was all clear of any active cancer. Truly a miracle! So now there is no way we would change our new lifestyle as it is far better than life before cancer. The whole experience has taught us how very precious life is and never to take it for granted. We live in the moment and enjoy each day. Love is the key and I have so much surrounding me from my family and wonderful friends. My wonderful husband has always remained positive and we share so much more than ever before.

I believe that another important part of my healing is that I have learnt to say NO. So I continue to set more realistic goals and look forward to the next half of my life with hope and joy. I no longer am afraid of cancer. I am certainly more in touch with my higher self and higher power.

I have a PEACE OF MIND now that is a priceless gift and my heart is full of gratitude."

Chapter Three
Understanding Emotional Anatomy

The most perceptive description that I have ever read on the movement of emotion was quoted from New York therapist Bonnie Bainbridge Cohen and it goes like this:

"The body is like the sand and emotion is like the breeze. It all depends on how the breeze is blowing as to the impressions that are left in the sand".

This quote succinctly describes the movement of emotional energy and its effects.

It takes a great deal of inner energy and strength to withhold, internalize or contain, what are natural emotional responses to life. When we are hurt, we cry. When we are happy, we smile and laugh. When we are deeply saddened, we grieve. We experience our emotions and they find their expression and liberation in laughter, joy, tears, and anger, to name but a few. Ideally we would be able to feel comfortable expressing those feelings rather than feeling bound to "keep a stiff upper lip" and soldier on. Repressing emotions can lead to a disturbing sense that we are not living true to ourselves; while it can lead to those around us believing that we can cope, when in reality we cannot. Repression of natural emotive responses is like trying to divert the course of a river. Just imagine your emotions flowing, moving like the waters of a river. When we live true to our nature we flow and experience life in a positive framework. When we repress our natural flow, especially to appease others, our river of emotion is held back against tremendous pressure like the damming of a river. Basically this is a model of how energy moves and flows or gets "stuck". We often feel or sense energy and its movement but we don't tangibly see it.

Energy is activity and will always move as a consequence of the process of change. Ultimately healing is the transformation and movement of energy. This is not a new idea and has been the basis of understanding in many ancient systems of medicine for many centuries. Physics is now lending credibility and meaning to the concept. In addition, the many theories about human consciousness have begun to see the science of physics taking on an almost cosmic or mystical role. However on a more day-to-day note, we work with and experience the qualities of emotional energy in our lives all the time. Have you ever been invited to dinner where the hosts had just had a major argument and try to pretend that all is well? You don't even need to see them when you enter the room to sense that an argument has transpired. Energy is powerful and it makes a strong statement.

The concepts of emotions and energy provide us with a framework for understanding the dynamics of our relationship to people and to the environment. Energy is constantly being transmitted and received. Our sensing, instinctive, intuitive selves deal with this in every-day relationships. Energy exchange touches upon two very important and essential issues which are not often discussed in health promotion or in healing the emotional aspects of breast cancer. The way this energy is contained or not contained by the individuals concerned is an important part of emotional health known as keeping *personal boundaries*. If you have difficulty saying NO to doing things you really don't want to do or you feel crumpled, crushed, deflated or fatigued after interactions with people in your environment, then you are likely to have a boundary issue. That is, you have difficulty in setting your energetic limits or, in other words, you allow people to move easily into your space. Interpersonal boundaries and how to deal with the challenge of relationship issues, whilst in the midst of a healing process, is the challenge that faces many women with breast cancer or other illness. The creation of healthy boundaries is a pivotal remedy as a part of our emotional healing, restoration of empowerment and the building of resilience. (Discussed fully in chapter twelve — **Boundaries**.)

Emotional Energy and the Body

Habitual responses, whether positive, negative, optimistic or pessimistic, over the course of our life, are recorded as stress responses and are stored in the body. Over a period of time these habitual patterns create what has been called our emotional anatomy. A simple example of this is the person with low self-esteem who rounds their shoulders and eventually adopts a stoop. Until recently the concept of body language has been used more by the corporate model than by the health and healing professions. Conditioning, belief systems, attitudes, self-esteem issues, joy and frustration in the workplace, all literally play their part in how we shape up. The body remembers and this is how emotional patterns become entrenched and stored in the musculature and other cells in the body. Just as the brain remembers, we also know that all cells remember our past experiences in a neurological and biochemical language of their own. These complex communication networks form the basis for the study of PNI (psycho-neuro-immunology), a relatively new science. At the forefront of this cellular frontier of discovery has been the awareness of how mind and emotion communicates with the body. This has now given credibility to the long held views of complementary medicine practitioners. That is, the shifts in attitude, lifestyle and making the connections of mind, body, emotions and spirit do form an holistic healing alliance. Our body will not only reflect life and how it has happened to us but also, and more importantly, how we have responded to life. If we embrace a healthy emotional life it mirrors in our body. If we habitually repress our emotions the reflection in the body mirror is one of stored tension, narrowing and contraction. There, our energy is contained or imprisoned waiting to be liberated like the unwinding of a coiled spring.

Ida Rolf, known for her work in structural integration, was quoted as saying: "The energy of the body exists in the relationship of the body structure to itself. If the structures are bound together, the energy is fixed (i.e. we are "stuck"). If the structures have a more fluid relationship the energy is less fixed and hence more abundant in its effects." For the purposes of recovery, when stuck emotional energy is liberated, more is made available for healing and wellbeing.

For the process of integration and restoration of health I believe that it is essential to liberate or discharge stored up energy (emotions); but my advice is *please be gentle with yourself when doing this.*

Remember that some of this material may have been bottled up for a long time. Time is a great healer and even more so in this case. Gentle release over a long period is recommended.

The simplicity of telling your life story, journal writing, clay work, writing poetry etc can all be ways of expressing bottled up feelings and emotions and giving a creative flow to their expression.

Jacqui's Story

Some people are capable of healing what to us seems the unhealable and Jacqui was one of these rare people. To bury a young child who has died is enough of a trauma. To bury your child as a result of a murder is one of the most heart-wrenching of human experiences. It is not hard to imagine the intensity of the emotions associated with this experience and what might happen if the Pandora's box of emotion was opened too quickly.

After several years of talk therapy she sought my assistance in dealing with her raw anger and grief as it was still affecting her life. I suggested that she consult a colleague of mine who worked in grief counselling and creative clay work. After many sessions and tears, Jacqui combined the energy of anger through her hands together with her repressed nurturing instincts as a mother to create in clay one of the most amazing headstones that I have ever seen. At the anniversary of her daughter's death, with a sense of ritual and feeling, the headstone was placed on the grave. That simple activity of working gently and creatively with the energy that had been held for so long had begun a process of healing for Jacqui. Eventually she developed a healthy tolerance and understanding of the actions of the perpetrator and she began to live again.

It is *imperative* that, as practitioners, we provide clients with the skills and tools so that they can build new health promoting habits and patterns. We must also take care to be gentle with ourselves and with them. Our job as practitioners should be to lead the way towards educating our clients to enact self-care and empowerment.

A Note of Caution

For the patient, client or practitioner, I caution the use of cathartic emotional release techniques for people with cancer. It requires a lot of energy to participate in some of these techniques but some in the past, despite my cautions, have paid very heavily indeed. Cancer patients or people with chronic disease often don't have the energy to engage in heavy psychotherapeutic practises.

One of the wonderful effects of a person simply telling their life story and having it honoured and being listened to, is that the process is, more often than not, a gentle one presenting an entree card for people to begin their healing process.

Check in with Your Emotions

Just as we examine and screen our breasts as a matter of attention to find lumps or bumps, maybe we should regularly screen our emotions too. Sometimes we can feel so removed from life that our emotional withholding can cause us to feel as if we are functioning on automatic pilot! Such is the effect of trauma. This state often requires the skilled help of a counsellor or psychotherapist. If you currently have emotional issues in your life and you are well, I encourage you to pay attention to them or at least have the intention to do so. To do so is better than denying or burying issues of importance which may ultimately affect your physical, mental, emotional and spiritual wellbeing. With the silence broken the healing and recovery process can begin.

Don't wait for the silence to break you.

If we are really honest with ourselves, we all know how we feel inside about issues, people and relationships. For example, we all know whether or not we feel happy, resentful, jealous or chronically disappointed. But what we do not seem to be aware of is how we handle the consequences of either repression or over expression of emotional material. No-one ever told us that care of our emotional health is just as important as, for example, maintaining and brushing our teeth. As a client recently wrote to me: "You represented a vital dimension in my healing — the unravelling of the emotional mystery within the breast".

Fatigue

One of the first early warning signs of breast cancer can be extreme fatigue that is not relieved by sleep or rest. This type of tiredness shows us that the chronic build-up of stress held in the mind is being mirrored in the body. It also demonstrates that we may have a boundary issue. We feel this as fatigue. As the build-up of stress in our inner and outer world becomes greater, there is often an impending sense of doom and powerlessness to do anything about it.

All too often women, being the carers and the nurturers, easily give and give of themselves. This giving may be just in relationship to her family; it may be in relation to giving her all to work; it may even be a combination of all this and more! It may be that a woman gives 150% of herself to her career and then becomes tired, jaded and unhappy with how her life has become. Another example might be a busy executive who is also a mother — torn between the need to be the perfect mother and to be perfectly available for her career. Knowing how impossible all this is; and all the time feeling that her attempts to nurture her job, her husband and children are just not working. Trying hard to meet all the demands, she silently keeps going and holds it all together despite feeling it is all just too much. These are the women who have trouble saying **NO** to things that they really don't want to do or feel they need to do for "approval". Fatigue is an obvious consequence of all this as "holding it all together" uses up a lot of energy. This pattern is a Catch 22 situation that results in boundaries becoming blurred or narrowed. Energetically, this has the effect of diminishing personal resilience, increased loss of energy and more fatigue. Thus starts a never-ending cycle that keeps repeating until *we* choose to end it by becoming empowered and resilient.

Learn to Listen to Yourself

Take heed — fatigue may be an early warning worth listening to. On a prevention basis, taking regular time out for yourself could be life saving. Fatigue, if unattended to in a woman who leads an active life, can develop into the next stage of the pattern that is the requirement for more and more willpower to keep the body going. In this scenario, no matter how exhausted a woman really feels, still there is the silence; and the tired body meekly follows along underneath a willful and strong head. After all, this woman knows a lot about stress, a lot about coping; it has always been her way. So, no matter how exhausted she is, this dependable woman is always there. But the inner woman begins to crave solitude. Finally she can no longer ignore the signals from within. She starts to get a sense of what is missing in her lifetime for herself! With the lack of personal space the inner tension begins to mount and finally she is confronted with the fact that she is living …

... "a lifestyle out of control,
Too much held too often has taken its toll."

Feeling powerless to act, feeling a sense of hopelessness to change, then the silence becomes sealed deep within. Paradoxically, however, the void is filled. It is filled with emotional, physical and spiritual pain that causes unrelenting ill ease! Women who have experienced breast cancer often talk of a feeling of impending doom. Despite instincts that are wounded, bodies that are tired and spirits that are low, it is not until diagnosis time that they have a reason or excuse to stop. Their inner life has demanded it.

Distorted, Nurturing, Twisted Emotions

Women easily develop a tendency to give of themselves by over-nurturing others and under-nurturing themselves in the giving of love. What causes this to happen and what is behind it all, is so often emotionally based. For example, with single women, the breakdown of a significant relationship that had been cherished and nurtured could be a key stress factor in the pattern of their breast cancer development. The detail of these traumatic experiences may be different for different people, but the pattern is so familiar. The way that I know how to make sense of this is, to listen to people's stories.

The following examples of life patterns are quite typical of how many women describe what their life was like before they developed breast cancer, how their fatigue developed and how it affected them.

First, women with breast cancer often notice that one positive benefit of having given so much of themselves and for having been there for everyone all the time was that "approval" came in large doses. This "giving of self" so often explains why women with breast cancer are thought of as being "nice" people. Of course they are "nice" — they are always helpful, always there. Typically they are the first to be at the school fete at 6 a.m. so that others do not have to get there so early.

Typically they are the women who also probably stayed up the night before baking scones, making jam and hemming a party dress for the favourite daughter. Breast cancer patients can be terrific mums, but they may sacrifice their energy to their own detriment! The danger for us, as women, is not to become enchanted by habitually living in what is called the "false self" system. A "false self" system is created from the bits and pieces of us that people like and hence we project the "nice" person in all our relations. In this circumstance, it is what happens to all the bits and pieces that people *don't like* that I am interested in. This is what Carl Jung named as ***shadow***.

Now some women can be perfectly contented, happy and healthy, giving freely of themselves. It is a fact that for some women, selfless service is an uncomplicated joy. But the key here is what drives that service and how well the woman nurtures herself. For if a woman has totally devoted her life to her family and she has never considered herself as an individual who also needs nurturing, she becomes very vulnerable. It is bound to happen that one day she will be left with no-one to give out to. With no experience of knowing how to give to herself and faced with a lack of nurturing from both the inside and the outside, the sudden awareness of the void within is felt. The "baby birds" have flown the nest, the nest is empty and suddenly so is life. I have seen this pattern in many women past the age of forty. It is as if their reason to be is no longer there.

Alternatively, a woman may be tirelessly giving out to her family and all goes well for a few years. Children grow, husbands get busy and people forget to notice what is being done for them. Now the "joy" of doing becomes the "resentment" of doing. The whole picture begins to take a downhill slide. Sadly, I recently met a woman in this situation who was dealing with very advanced secondary breast cancer, and who, despite loving her family, resented everything about her life with them. She was very "stuck" in this pattern and was so incredibly "silent" that she was almost paralysed and unable to communicate at all. Trapped as she was — trapped in an endless cycle of resentment, suffering and self pity from which it seemed no-one could retrieve her — she did confide in me saying that she just wanted to go. She was tired of living. She died two weeks later.

Linda's Story

Linda discovered a breast lump that was confirmed to be cancerous. At that time she refused a mastectomy and just had the lump removed. This was followed with thirty days of radiotherapy. At the time Linda had just returned from a period of living in the United States.

"I had worked as a receptionist/assistant in a holistic medical clinic there and had seen many people getting well. My marriage had collapsed in America and when I came back to Australia, deep inside, I really wanted to die. I felt I couldn't do it directly to myself; however I believe the cancer decided to try to do it for me. However, once I had the surgery and began radiation, I was getting pretty cross with myself for wanting to die — just because someone else didn't think I was good enough! So I began using meditation, active visualisation and vitamin and mineral supplements. Because I only had the lump out, I had a heavy treatment schedule. Yet, despite the warnings of pain and other side effects, I was the only one of the ten ladies who went through with me that had no problems.

For the first time this caused me to begin to feel that I could **have some power over my own life**. That was really exciting! Since then however, there have been some lapses in faith. Eighteen months after the surgery, a nodule appeared in my thyroid. I requested one month to work on it and sure enough it decreased. Now, if I get stressed, up it comes. I intensify the efforts, regain the balance, down it goes. I seem able to control it.

Through all this, I came to know that those who faced death and saw it as a new beginning could let go and have a good death. That has helped me a lot. You know my mother often told me as a child that she wanted to die. I'm sure this made a deep impression on my developing psyche. I have had trouble getting over it fully and I know that for years it interfered with me maintaining my joy of life. It has been a strong emotional habit to break. Now, with a renewed spiritual vigour, I pray a lot and know that I would not have made it without prayer. At the moment I want to work on myself. I am in a conventional job and my husband is back in my life. I am learning a lot about male and female relationships.

I believe I got cancer in the breast because I was not nurturing myself. When my children were young I used to have these horrible nightmares. I was suckling this thin, wretched, whimpering child who had a smelly nappy on and appeared so uncared for. I could never understand it, as I gave everything I had to my children. Only recently, when I was sick, did I realise that the child was myself!

Now I don't flagellate myself. **I can accept myself** and where I am at in my life. I continue to meditate and get closer to my spiritual self. I aim to change slowly. I have good days and bad ones, but mostly they are good. Cancer has pointed me in the right spiritual direction. I have learnt how the mind, emotions and spirit control the body. The material and worldly things have become less important, although I still love to go out, dress up and have fun. I have met and shared my new life with so many people that I now have a better perspective. I also believe that death, as a conscious experience, is very important — especially if it is a part of living."

Self Mastery

It seems that the need to take control of one's life when dealing with breast cancer comes up time and time again. In the process of healing, this is a necessity, according to those who have healed. We lose control in so many ways, so easily and so often for reasons that may have apparently noble causes. Loss of control, however, ultimately leads to a loss of spirit or power.

Some define healing as bringing your spirit home, or taking your power back consciously and methodically from all the people to whom you have given it away. This taking control of one's life again goes hand in hand with taking responsibility for yourself and for your life. It is a huge step to take. This is not the only important step in the realm of self-help approaches in healing. Having control and the power of choice in all treatments can really make a difference to the outcome. In order to survive, you may have to speak up, ask questions and assert yourself when necessary. Remember, it is your body and it will be you who will ultimately live with the consequences of whatever approach you choose.

Chapter Four

Examining the Causes of Breast Cancer

One of my interests has been collecting old medical books, some of which date back as far as 1765. One such book called *Buchan's Medecine* published in Edinburgh, contains a brilliant paragraph about the causes of breast cancer, as understood at that time. As you will see the parallels with todays complementary and medical approaches are astonishingly evident.

"Persons after the age of forty five, particularly women, and those who lead an indolent sedentary life are most subject to this disease.

This disease is often owing to suppressed evacuations; hence it proves to be frequently fatal to women of gross habit, particularly old maids and widows about the time when the menstrual flux ceases. It may likewise be occasioned by excessive fear, grief, anger, religious melancholy, or any of the depressing passions. Hence the unfortunate, the choleric, and those persons who devote themselves to a religious life in convents or monasteries, are often afflicted with it.

It may be occasioned by the long-continued use of food that is too hard of digestion, or of an acrid nature; by barrenness; celibacy; indolence; cold; blows; friction; pressure; or the like. Women often suffer from the last of these, by means of their stays, which squeeze and compress their breast as to occasion great mischief. Sometimes the disease is owing to a hereditary disposition."

Examining this in light of today's knowledge we find that there is current evidence about:

- Chronic constipation as a contributing factor to breast cancer.

- Excessive exposure to X-rays (yourself and/or parents).
- Increased risk for breast cancer at the time of menopause especially if one has not had children.
- The emotional factors: now recognised as a contributing factor prior to, at diagnosis and towards recovery.
- Healthy relationships being a health promoting and longevity factor.
- Dietary factors: Poor digestion and the eating of foods that are difficult to digest (e.g. excessive meat and low fibre).
- Women who do not breast feed are thought to have a higher risk of breast cancer. Stimulation, touch, sucking of the nipple is thought to be a helpful preventive.
- Pressure and friction caused in this century particularly by the design of women's brassieres. Ill fitting and under-wire bras have been implicated in research to be a possible causative factor. This is due to the inability of breast tissue to move and the lymphatic system to be able to adequately drain the breast.
- Geneticists have identified some breast cancers as having strong hereditary components.

We now live in an age where causes of disease have become a little more complex due to industrialisation and the stresses and strains of modern living in a highly competitive world. One of the biggest contributions to breast cancer and indeed cancer in general, are environmental chemicals and pollutants; in particular, chemicals known as hormone disrupters. DDT is thought to have had a very detrimental effect. Excessive exposure to radiation and low frequency electromagnetic energy, ingested carcinogens, (cancer-causing agents, e.g. pesticides), fungicides and other contaminants in the food chain and of course cigarette smoking are all known causes of breast cancer.

Some of these things are so much a part of modern living and the levels of contamination are so high that it may be a process of adapting to them rather than eradication. Be careful not to become too fanatical. But there is much that *you can do* by making healthy choices. That is, consider where your food comes from and that you buy as fresh as possible, organically or bio-dynamically grown (or raised if meat, cheese, milk etc). Keep your diet loaded with fresh vegetables and fruits and eat less meat. If possible keep it high in fibre content therefore avoiding constipation. There is researched evidence that more than twenty eight grams of fibre intake daily helps the body to eliminate some of the toxic materials mentioned above and therefore helps to prevent breast and bowel cancer as well as promoting health in general.

If we are feeling healthy inside, we are also of a happier disposition and more resistant to some illnesses. A friend of mine who is a medical doctor in Australia tells his patients that happiness is an empty rectum! Albert Schweitzer was quoted as saying: *"Illness never stayed too long with me, I am too inhospitable a host"*.

The good news is that if you maintain a healthy lifestyle, your chances of surviving adversity of all kinds, whether it is disease or life-changing circumstances, is far greater. However, just because you do live a healthy lifestyle does not make you immune to life's crises and traumas. Building your inner resilience as a part of that healthy lifestyle *will* positively affect your outcome to flourish when under challenge. Each of us has to decide for ourselves and our families what choices we will make and what responsibilities we will take towards our healthcare and self-care. The old proverb rings true: *"An ounce of prevention is worth a pound of cure"*.

How Emotions Can Make or Break Us

First of all I do not believe that emotions of themselves can be classified as negative. All emotional expression can be positive. If emotion is held onto for a period of time, its release can be demonstrated to have more intensity than the original emotion. If we learn to speak our truth and express ourselves regularly we do not suffer from a backlog of emotional material and we feel better for it. To me the only negative emotion is one that has had a lid put on it!

Following on with the understanding of emotional issues and health when we hold our silence, withhold our feelings, withhold our love, withhold the nurturing of ourselves, we stifle our passion, our *joie de vivre*. The ability to hold silence and adopt a passive approach that is not a part of a woman's natural character is equivalent to putting a tight lid on a saucepan that is trying to boil over!

A woman called Sally in a recent group programme shared this story with us. As a woman currently dealing with breast cancer, she told of how her family had been concerned for her health before her diagnosis. For a long time she was always stressed, feisty and became angry easily. Also her family had been having trouble coping with vocalising and, what to them was, erratic behaviour. In fact this was Sally's way of releasing stress; a way of "talking it out aloud". So, without dealing with the background of her anger and stress issues, Sally tried to adopt a new way of coping and, in her words, "bit her tongue" whenever she felt she wanted to be vocal. She was trying hard to be a "nice" person especially in her workplace. However, the result was that Sally went about her daily business feeling like an unexploded volcano! She was not used to living her life to please other people and, after all, according to Sally, she had plenty of things in her life to be fiery about! Within a year, Sally began to experience extreme fatigue and lethargy. A general checkup with her GP resulted in a breast lump being detected and the biopsy results diagnosed the lump to be malignant. As a consequence a large portion of breast was removed. She took the opportunity in one of our groups to use her keen and feisty wit. She said to her husband sitting next to her "Well, see where all this got me. Thank God I've got a good excuse now to go back to being my old self again! I need to be me and not what other people would like me to be." Surprisingly, his response was one of relief too and he commented that he too might get a reward by getting back the woman he married!

Quote from "Isaac Davis in Manhattan" by Woody Allen and Marshal Brickman.

"Well, I don't get angry, okay? I mean I have a tendency to internalize. I can't express anger. That's one of the problems I have. I grow a tumour instead."

Sometimes for a couple, a life-threatening illness can be the wake up call for not only the healing of an illness but the healing of a relationship. The illness can provide an opening for expressing issues that for some people could never be tackled in the normal course of their life.

People grow apart for all sorts of reasons. Time goes by, communication ebbs away due to the *busy-ness* of life. Sadly the reverse is also true. If a relationship has been a silent battleground, the illness can be the voice that eventually demands change. Women often know this; but can be too fearful to take independent action especially if they are dependent on partners for finance and stability or if there are children involved. Some women have feared the consequences of change so much that they have chosen to do nothing at all. This is why it has been important for me to develop attainable methods that simplify the process of change. It is also important to mention that change is perceived as a stress for many people. Change that is lasting comes from personal awareness and a desire to change. You cannot make anyone change, even if you perceive it is in his or her best interests. So beware; if only one partner changes, this can put even more strain on a relationship; trying to do so is not only crossing their boundaries; but it will cause you stress and frustration.

As emotion is felt, it finds its expression in the outer world, with what we experience as happiness, joy, excitement, love, grief, anger, resentment, rage and so on. My definition of depression is the absolute non-movement of emotion, characterized by a blankness of expression or feeling. Depression can be the outward manifestation of long-term imploded passion, an inability to live your truth.

However, what if a woman felt depressed, dis-spirited and tried to pretend that all in life was sunny and wonderful? I ask where would the energy of depression go? It would still be there. It would still exist in the mind, the psyche and the body, but it would be blocked from finding outer expression.

The following exercise may help to clarify this. Close your eyes for a moment and think of a time when you experienced spontaneous happiness in your life. Maybe it was a surprise or good news of some kind. As you think about that time, consciously go through the memories, imagine the scene, the tastes, smells, sounds and sensations and notice how these memories have feelings associated with them. Experience those feelings for a few moments; notice the effects of the memories and then open your eyes. If you re-experienced a truly happy and joyful event, you will notice a sense of good feeling in the body. Your immune system is likely to have responded in a positive way; maybe now you also have a sense of the animated movement of emotional energy. But what happens if we hold in that emotional energy and what could cause us to do so?

As previously discussed, it is the emotional material that other people don't like that we are likely to "bottle up" inside. These emotions are also the ones that literally "eat holes" in us. It seems, however, that we are not so likely to do it with the so-called positive emotions in life; that is, the put on a happy face mentality. We are often taught from a very young age that this is what is acceptable. Again it is about keeping the "stiff upper lip", "keeping the peace" and being "nice". It all seems to depend on our behavioural type. Some people can adapt and live the above quite obediently, while other types of people cannot, and so from an early age they construct a false self from which they live their life. In some cultures this ethic is more entrenched than others thus making personal change more difficult in the face of the status quo. Fear of not being accepted by the people we love is a key reason why women struggle with change.

Women with breast cancer often demonstrate this and it can take many different forms of expression. One of the symptoms of this is women's tendency to give out care and love to everyone else around, while at the same time finding difficulty in accepting the love that is being given to them. At the root of this problem is an inability to give love to themselves — to be self-nurturing. This, in my experience, revolves around a chronic lack of self-esteem or self-worth and is often the product of long-term conditioning. Often there is a sense of emotions being devalued or being perceived by the woman to be devalued. The full or partial loss of a breast can be devastating to a woman whose self-esteem is already damaged. Many of my breast cancer patients have strongly identified with this aspect in their own experience.

This pattern of emotional suppression or denial can and often does lead on to extreme fatigue. Living the false self can be exhausting. Women have often described this as feeling "sick at heart". So, with their "battery flat", women often have to drive on, using sheer willpower and masking their inner fatigue in order to survive. Often these women have great difficulty asking for help, because they are the people that everyone has learned to rely upon and as a result they have little ability to say "no". They could not possibly let people down!

No-one lives in a vacuum in this world and stress generated from one's outer life experience only adds to the load. The internal stress from withholding and the external stress of living means that somewhere, somehow, something has to give. It is usually a woman's health that pays the price presenting them with a definite ultimatum for change and transformation — breast cancer. The following story of Dallas' brush with breast cancer highlights some of the above points. The way she tells her story reflects her true nature now, which she demonstrates with good humour and verve!

Dallas' Story

Dallas had a biopsy for a suspicious thickening in her breast although it was three days before the positive diagnosis of cancer was confirmed. According to Dallas "the initial reaction was panic. Really, I felt like I was looking possible death in the eyeball. I thought of the family particularly and how they would cope. I didn't cry during the day and no-one knew or picked it up. The nights were the worst. Every so often I would get this feeling of blind panic. After the three days I had sorted it out and prepared myself. Surgery was recommended immediately but I wanted to make sure it had not spread and insisted on scans. These were clear but after the surgery it was found that two lymph nodes were affected. The surgeon described the cancer as a "virulent little bastard!" and wanted me to have chemo. He spent hours convincing me to have the treatment as I was concerned about it depressing my immune system. I realised that I had no other choice and so I began a twelve-month course. It was hell and the worst year of my life. I managed to keep working, just taking five days off each month. But it was not just how sick it left me feeling but the other things with the body. I guess I do resent it in many ways because of the changes that took place in my body, some of them permanent. I experienced premature menopause, hot flushes, the loss of taste and smell and the hypersensitivity to some things. Aerosol sprays still nearly make me throw up. I guess I kept going for the children mostly. At first all the family were keen for me to have it but after three months they wanted me to stop. I guess I felt I had committed myself and told myself it was going to work, so I stuck with it. The hardest bloody twelve months of my life!

However, it was really quite humbling through all this to become aware of the incredible number of people who were so caring. It made me more aware of what makes the world go around. As well the friendships that developed with the other women going through the chemo were helpful. They reminded me that I wasn't alone and that there were women in much worse situations than myself."

Twelve months of chemotherapy completed, Dallas then discovered that she had cervical dysplasia.

"I overheard it actually at the doctors. It seems they didn't tell me at the first sign — three months earlier as they didn't want to worry me! At the second test the area affected was clearly visible. It was then that I thought that I had to do something for myself. I had always believed in the power of the mind but was unsure of how to use it, so, I began talking to this area of my body and pretty simply told the problem to go away. I took charge of my life and attended a residential programme for people with cancer. This gave me the tools to work with, although by that time the dysplasia had cleared anyway. My main focus though was to stay well from then on.

If I get tired now I know I get problems. It's very important to keep yourself on an even keel. I do that with meditation, managing stress in my life, diet and attitude. The meditation helps with the kids too. After a good session in the morning, even a little monster can't touch me, try as they might!

Cancer has brought a new perspective to my life. In the long term it has led to a sorting out of priorities. I now appreciate people more and see things through different eyes. I appreciate the country even more, take time to look at something — a simple thing that is really beautiful. It's a heightening of awareness. Things that I was vaguely aware of before, and took for granted in fact, are now so wonderful.

Relationships have changed a bit. I am less inclined to let others organise my time for me now. I am much more aware of the value of time and my need to control it. And, I am probably less tolerant of crap — you know, from other people. I either avoid it or I am more direct; say what I think and express my opinion more. I am not so prepared to compromise myself and put up with it."

Understanding Our Choices

As a product of our experience and perceptions of early life we may be pre-programmed to internalize feelings that otherwise we would be better off releasing. During the difficult and traumatic times of our lives we learn to cope in particular ways. These ways may be a great help to us in the future, or they may not, depending on who we are as individuals and whether the adopted style of coping allows us to *live true to our nature*. Swiss herbalist Dr Alfred Vogel used to say: *"People become ill because they do not wear their nature well!"*

It seems there is little doubt that the emotional and psychological environment in which we grew up has an enormous impact. The influence of parents and other people close to us, has quite an influence on our emotional responses and our ability to express our emotions. Clearly, as children, we often adopt subconsciously, or even consciously, attitudes and behaviours of those close to us. Even if we try to fight against being like our mother or father, one day your husband might say to you in a heated moment:

"You're getting more like your mother every day. That's what she would have said ...!"

And the same can be said of wives to husbands as well:

"You know, you are just like your father. Can't you just try to feel a little more ...?"

This pattern of conditioned learning at a young age is termed "premature cognitive commitment" which basically means that we make a commitment to a certain way of learning how to be, at an early age. This "setting" of responses is often the reason why many people find great difficulty accepting and activating change in their lives. Their commitment or habitual response to continue that commitment is so strong, so embedded, that it has become part of their life's belief system.

A simple behavioural experiment conducted with flies can explain this point! If you place a number of flies in a jar covered with wire they will happily fly around and around perceiving that the jar is "their space". Eventually, when the wire is removed, the flies have an obvious escape route. However, although we have given them the opportunity to fly out and away, the majority of them will stay within the confines of the jar! They have made a behavioural "commitment" that the jar is where they are to stay. Only one or two "pioneer" flies will leave the jar and escape! The "pioneer" flies symbolize the adventurers who recognise another way, a way out of the jar. They do not fulfil their commitment to stay "stuck" in the confines of what "should" or "might" happen to them if they take a risk! Like Dallas in her story — she knew there had to be another way, risked the change of being true to herself again and that she needed to learn to help herself.

Our perceptions, the way we view the world and our resulting behaviour, are all influenced by these early experiences. In any traumatic situation or challenge, we clearly do the best we can at the time. In considering all of this, be gentle with yourself. Some of the ways we have used to cope in the past, we may not feel so good about now and, importantly, they may no longer be effective. But remember back to that time. What else did we know? What else could we have done? At least we can congratulate ourselves for making it through at all. We may be a little worn around the edges, but we are still here! Do not beat yourself up!

Obviously some of our patterns of behaviour have been quite effective, perhaps even essential in helping us through particular life crises. Perhaps the stifled silence was the only way we could keep the peace, endure a tragedy and keep going. The brain exhibits quite amazing survival skills when required. The question is do we still want to keep doing that (like the flies in the jar)? Have we now got other options (the lid is removed from the jar) and would doing it differently work better for us now? **The "pioneer" flies find a new way of behaving, break the learned habit and liberate themselves from the jar.**

Sexual Abuse and Chronic Ill Health

For some women, their early life history may be more important than for others. This is particularly so for those women who have experienced major personal tragedies, such as sexual abuse. This issue needs to be given a voice as so many women with breast cancer, so many *Women of Silence*, have shared their hidden grief or guilt about it with me. It is by nature an emotionally charged subject but I feel that often it is an essential ingredient in healing the feminine, if that aspect has been damaged. If it is a part of a woman's emotional history, it also needs to be a part of her current recovery and healing agenda.

If I had not had so many stories volunteered and shared with intense sincerity over the years, I might have presumed that coincidence was at play here. However, this has been such a common issue, not only for women dealing with breast cancers, but female reproductive cancers of all kinds, that I feel impelled to share it. Please understand that this may have been an important issue for some, but clearly **NOT ALL** women with breast cancer.

I have given the following section a great deal of consideration due to its intimate and powerful nature. Choosing to exclude it could leave a cloud of unknowing for the many women who, in reality, have faced sexual abuse in their lives and who already know or sense that this event has some significance in their illness and accordingly some significance in their recovery.

Basically there are three groups of women to whom this issue of sexual abuse applies.Those who are aware of abuse and are basically well. Those who have an illness such as breast cancer and thirdly those who have an uncomfortable suspicion that more has happened to them than they consciously remember. I hope that this discussion may open the door for those women who so far are basically healthy, have experienced sexual abuse in their lives, but feel helpless to resolve it and therefore have been withholding it entirely. If you identify with this I do encourage you to seek the help of a psychotherapist or counsellor.

The issue of unresolved sexual abuse seems to be linked to female health problems such as chronic vaginitis, cervical dysplasia, frigidity, difficulty and pain with periods and a wide variety of other conditions. Quite often the subject is broached by the statement, "I don't know if this has anything to do with my condition but ..." the story unfolds with a tone of relief that implies: "At last this is someone I can tell." The silence is broken and healing and recovery can begin.

The second group of women are those who have been already given a diagnosis of cancer, whether it be in the breast or reproductive areas. These women have often been very conscious of the fact that sexual abuse was an issue in their lives and when their diagnosis came, often they were not surprised. My experience here too, is that although they were fully aware that this issue had affected them in the past, and was still affecting them in their current life, they had not sought help or spoken about it with anyone. It was only when the illness developed and they joined in with a group, only when they saw and related to other people in similar difficulties, that the "ice was broken". Finally they could speak after years of self-imposed silence. In private counselling, the problem of prolonged frigidity often comes up in conversation.

I can remember a time during a residential group where a courageous middle aged woman spoke about her life to the group, announcing that she had been a victim of incest. Her husband, also in the room, was extremely shocked and surprised. He had not known. However, he did say that sexual relations had always been difficult for them and now at least it made some sort of sense to him. Fortunately their relationship was rock solid, so together they worked it out. The woman's newly found ability not to remain silent and her husband's ability to be understanding, patient and particularly caring provided a wonderful platform for opening communication and healing their relationship on all levels. I am constantly aware of how different people need all kinds of different things in order to heal. That is the mystery for each to discover. This one episode was a key for her. She began to respond to her chemotherapy treatment after that time and recovered fully.

Finally, to the third and last group. For these women, the problem of sexual abuse has not been obvious. Initially it was not within the grasp of the women's conscious minds. However, they did have an innate awareness of some aspect of their sexual feelings being peculiar and that sexual relationships had always been a difficult area of their life. Most of these women I have come to know quite well and they will still contact me for a chat. It seems that their recovery can be quite a long one and maybe this is due to the fact that their abuse was buried and out of conscious awareness for such a long time.

It was not until my first two patients with repressed abuse problems were in the final stages of dying that they actually spoke of it. This made me aware that maybe their outcomes could have been different. With both these women I had been aware of some sort of enormous pain and my "gut feeling" was that abuse of some kind had taken place. In order to make survival possible, the entire event had been filed away, out of conscious access. However, through the process of meditation and coming to peace with themselves, the fragmented and repressed issues of their lives were dealt with and were shared with their partners just prior to death.

Importantly, however, I do believe that these women, at the end of their lives found healing. Both their partners wrote to me of their experiences with great sensitivity and understanding. They also commented that these open discussions prior to the death of their wives enabled them to understand and to cope better with their grief afterwards. One comment I would make to anyone who is choosing to repress or not heal these old wounds is simply this: "Is it worth dying for?"

These days I refer people to specialist counsellors, psychotherapists or psychiatrists for guidance if I suspect that sexual abuse may be involved in a woman's history.

It can take a long time to recover and a lot of time to rebuild trust and safety. Jenny's story may help to share the significance of this issue in this third group of women. The women who suspect abuse which has been a part of their lives tend to have forgotten it and buried it in the unconscious mind. However, the body remembers where the mind absents itself.

Jenny's Story

Jenny had endured a long struggle with secondary cancer after an initial mastectomy. She often experienced a great deal of inner tension and feelings of generally not being at ease with herself. However, she found great solace in reconnecting with her religion. She had been highly passionate about it many years ago but for some unknown reason had let it slip away out of her life. She was experiencing deep feelings of guilt about many things and found her reconnection with the church a great source of comfort. Over a period of time her spirit and determination to heal was getting stronger and stronger, but her physical condition was becoming weaker. Rarely had I observed such passion to heal in a patient who was so ill for so long.

It took two years of group and individual work as well as several visits to a psychiatrist, before the silence of prolonged sexual abuse was ready to be dealt with. By this time however, Jenny had learned many skills and was spiritually able to cope with facing the past and the insidious effects it was having on her life now. Sometimes people like Jenny can have an awareness of an issue but feel they are too disempowered to deal with it. The intention to deal with it when *they* are ready is not to be ignored. Some time later she related to me how she innately knew that the sexual area of her life was badly out of balance because of something really major but she had no idea what was the cause. I found it interesting that she said the following, "It was as if my body knew, my body remembered what had happened to it, especially when my husband came near me at night. I would go sort of rigid. It was as if my entire sexuality would go into "shut-down". I

56

just couldn't let go. We attended marriage counselling for some time, but it didn't help."

But now Jenny's burden was beginning to lift after re-experiencing the memory of these painful events. There was in fact a veritable Pandora's box of abuse. However, she courageously "faced the tiger" and piece by piece, began to restore the fragments of her life into wholeness. Jenny had been gang raped at twelve. Her mother blamed her for enticing the boys concerned and bringing shame upon the family. The case went to court and several of the young men went to prison. Jenny felt imprisoned by shame. However a story that had not emerged until well into the process of her illness was the following. There was another story behind the story that told of a young girl who had been sexually abused for many years by her father. As a pubescent girl, Jenny became her father's mistress and had to go through the rape experience as well! She resented her mother and does not know whether or not she knew of the incest. Every time her mother was away, which was often, her father would make her appease his needs. It seems he had a particular appetite for groping and handling her breasts. When she married her breast area became, in her words, "a no go zone". Her experiences had led her to great guilt, shame and a sense of powerlessness that left her feeling empty and alone, but still she loved and cared for her father enormously. She was "his little princess". With no framework in which to make sense of all this and the obvious silence that surrounded the entire experience, Jenny's personality changed and she wore the personal guilt, blame, shame and silence for many years.

In order to heal her life rather than just her cancer, Jenny began the process of forgiving her father. She also forgave the young men who had taken advantage of her sexuality and negated her power of choice. She said that due to her religious feelings, she could now do it, but that actually the hardest part was forgiving herself; learning to let go of the guilt and the shame and the feeling that her illness had been a justified punishment for her actions.

"Ridding myself of my breast didn't rid myself of my problems but maybe it gave me more time to deal with them", she said.

Jenny felt as if the weight of the world was off her shoulders. With her humour returned she once commented, "I guess I've got it off my chest at last!" She was most grateful to the kind and patient psychiatrist, a colleague of mine, who consistently helped her over many years. I enjoyed her company and from time-to-time we would meet for an informal chat. Her marriage was not in good shape and this always concerned her. Despite painful bone secondaries, Jenny believed that she was healed in spirit and bravely continued her struggle for survival.

I followed Jenny's progress over many years, but sadly she committed suicide following the lack of solutions to chronic problems that had developed within her marriage. She had been through treatments for the bone secondaries and had responded well and apparently she had experienced recurrences in both her lymphatic system and eventually in the other breast which was also removed. Her cancer was in remission at the time of her death.

This woman was one of the bravest souls I have met within my practice and I am certainly enriched for having known her. Clearly she had had enough. I delivered the eulogy at her funeral and stood by her graveside as the thunder rolled overhead and the lightning flashed around us and her spirit moved in the wind.

It remains a mystery why some people's lives are as they are and why, at such a young age, some people are challenged with issues way beyond their years and means to manage. A Filipino healer that I know imparted some wisdom when I spoke with her of Jenny's story. She simply said to me:

"All diseases are curable, all people are not!"

As difficult as it may be to write about these unpleasant facts of life, I am impelled and encouraged by the women who have had this experience to deal with and have spoken about the relief that comes from breaking the silence. No, the memories are not removed, but the emotional sting, the inner hurt, the inner pain can be dealt with and, although wounded deeply, as with most wounds that heal — scars form. Clarissa Pinkola Estes calls this group of women the *scar clan*. Congratulate yourself that you have survived; you have made it through one of the most traumatic issues that could ever be in a woman's life. Now, make the transition from surviving to thriving, speak when you feel ready to, seek the help and wise counsel you need and begin to regain the passion for life that still dwells within.

I will share with you the wise words of a sign that appeared on one of our local churches. This saying reflected Jenny's new philosophy of living and dying:

"When trouble overtakes you
Let God take over!"

Jenny believed that the ordeals that life presents do not have punishment as their goal but rather they offer an opportunity for transformation.

Chapter Five

Reclaim Your Magic

So how can you recover not only your life but also your "magic"? What would you need to do? What changes would you make? Equally important is the question of what would stop you from making those changes? The first two questions are easy for most to answer. Often it is the answer to the last question that is the most significant.

Making personal changes and transformations can be like leaping off the precipice into the unknown. This can become even more risky if your health is frail but it can be the very challenge that can turn obstacles into opportunities! Remember always — that the only real freedom we have in this life is to choose how we respond to it. People who demonstrate a survivor personality often have had many experiences in their life that have shaped them into the people we are in awe of. They too have come to crossroads in their lives, often through means other than illness, that have clearly demanded changes. Importantly, survivors realised at that point that they had a choice — a choice of how they would respond. These are the people who made the courageous decision to "face the tiger" and discovered once they had faced it, that it was not nearly so scary but held something quite wonderful, quite "magical".

For example, they are people who climb mountains in order to reach that special moment of "magic" — the magic of reaching the pinnacle and viewing the world from its highest point. The epiphany. Life can be full of magic moments. Although money gives you options, it cannot buy the fundamental happiness that is experienced by people who know, love and accept themselves, people who dare to live their truth.

Many years ago I had the pleasure of spending some time with the late Sir Edward "Weary" Dunlop who had been a doctor with the POW's on the tragic Burma railway during the second world war. One incident we spoke about was when he was charged with insubordination and was to be executed. In fact, this happened to him many times and he spoke humbly and gratefully about all of his reprieves. Facing the fear of his imminent demise, he realised that he had a choice about how he responded to the crisis. He had watched the demise of other men who had surrendered to the fear and saw themselves as doomed and hopeless. I am not surprised that he was to become a leading cancer surgeon, whose patients adored him for his compassion, wit and optimism especially when the prognosis was poor. Not only was he able to help them with their physical problems but he had an innate understanding of their suffering and the fear of the unknown that they were facing. He was therefore able, through his presence, to lend them the courage to go on, to heal and to reclaim their "magic". Survivorship is not an elite club; anyone can join, all you need is hope. The art of survival is innate in us all. Take the opportunity, "seize the day" and "seize the moment".

The Challenge of Change

Many people incorrectly believe that change will strip them of their identity or that life-changes are too demanding especially at a time when energy is low and fatigue is high. To a certain extent this is a reality; people with cancer must be very aware of how they expend their energy. But change, in its essence, may not be as demanding as you believe it to be. Many of our key relationships hinge on the identity that we have constructed over many years, perhaps even over a lifetime. Change is like taking off masks or layers to discover your-self rather than trying to change into something that you are not. It is about *be-coming* because the real and true self is there all the time. If you change in order to please others it tends to have a short shelf life as does trying to change without the sustaining deep commitment and awareness that is necessary. The biggest obstacle to change is that we are often scared that if people see and know who we really are, they may not like what they see! We may lose approval and we may lose love. This is a genuine obstacle for some, as the fear associated with change and being authentic, seems too great a risk to take.

The first step is deciding that you want to do it! At this point intention becomes the imperative instigator to allow the possibilities to open up and the "magic" to happen. Interestingly this does not necessarily mean that the illness will be resolved. Women have told me that they have reached a place in their journey where they feel as if they could live or die and "know" that they would be okay. This is because touching the inner "magic" gets us in touch with who we really are. Then we can begin the most intimate relationship with ourselves and it will radiate to all around us. A colleague of mine used to express the word intimacy as *in-to me-see*!

The first hint of "magic" working in your life on an outer level may manifest itself in the sudden influx of apparent coincidences known as synchronicities. This might be termed a state of heightened conscious awareness where you become more open to receive new information or interpret old information differently. For instance, a book may fall from a shelf and when you look down, there before you are the answers to a problem or a question that you have been giving serious thought to. A friend may make a comment that provides a significant insight for you, just at the right time. Inspiration is around us in abundance if we can open ourselves to the possibilities.

During my ex-husband's illness we experienced many difficulties with finances. For a while I worked part time to support the extras that we needed; but as time went on this became impossible. Amazingly, money would appear when we needed it often sent anonymously in cash or as bank cheques. Like the birds of the air, we were never without seed.

These little glimpses of the nature of "magic" and synchronicity can lead the way into a deeper level of "ancient magic" that runs so deep, it feels as if it flows in our blood and through to our very souls. For women, this "old magic" comes from the instinctive, intuitive, feminine principle that is now waking up and offering us access to a storehouse of wisdom. It probably carries the innate wisdom of all the women who have gone before you; it is like a blueprint of feminine energy.

I once heard a wonderful talk by Jungian analyst Robert Johnson on the *Transformations of Life*. He stated that a woman who is living true to her nature, never really leaves the hall of wisdom and therefore never needs to search for wisdom in the outside world for it dwells within her all the time. Men on the other hand, he said, need to search for the experience in the outer world in order to be initiated and re-connected to their wisdom. They need to go off on their quests of courage and bravery to find out who they are.

As women enter their hall of wisdom, where the "old magic" lies, it is as if we become in tune or rhythm with the sound and cycles of our hearts and souls. This experience is accessible to all women. It knows no social, ethnic or financial boundary. It is inside for the finding! I have recognised this quality in some of the poorest women in India and throughout many parts of Asia. I have experienced its presence and power in Afro-American women and in Australian Aboriginal women. These are women of their own power who know how to connect with the "magic"; that "sacred magic" which provides such unique sustenance in a woman's life. Without it, she never feels complete, and if she mistakenly takes the masculine path into the outside world to provide her with sustenance, she will always be feeling hungry and undernourished — and wondering why.

This state of "inner magic" can neither be controlled nor touched by knowledge, reason or rational thinking. It just is. I know I was able to tune in to this level of understanding when my ex-husband was in the midst of his cancer experience and I know the strength I drew from it. It sustained me throughout and it still fuels me to continue on.

Chapter Six

Heal with Zeal

The Application to Breast Cancer

Being able both to observe your life and experience it at the same time, brings with it great benefits. This is called living in the moment. You will begin to notice how situations or people that used to bother you or things you used to feel impelled to hold on to, can no longer penetrate your boundary or invoke a stress response. Because you have meditated in the body you will know your body very well, and the observer part of you will give you an alert signal as if to say "be careful you are vulnerable right now". If this is the case, you will become aware of feeling stressed and you will be able to locate the sensation that the stressor has made somewhere in your body. If you notice it you can then remedy the situation. Our health is affected when we either don't notice or we deny what we are sensing in our bodies. We can remedy the situation by, for example, moving away from a circumstance or person who is challenging us. If we cannot move away then we need to use our tools for building resilience and boundaries.

Healing the Feminine

We have already identified that tension can be stored in the muscles of the body and that it is also reflected in the way women breathe. The solar plexus is another key area. This is a particularly sensitive area for women and is an area where withheld emotions and feelings are registered and stored. Women can be injured psychically and emotionally in this vulnerable place known as the void. Disruption to the solar plexus can wreak havoc with women's health. If we look at this in terms of the void within, there is an involvement with the repression of gut feelings created by the lack of the living of our truth. When the void begins to become overloaded, in women, we call the process a mid-life crisis. The following poem by Victorian poet Emily Dickinson describes this void and the process so eloquently:

> *There is a pain so utter,*
> *It swallows substance up,*
> *Then covers the abyss with trance*
> *So that memory can step around, across, upon it.*
> *As one within a dream goes swooning.*
> *Where an open eye would drop him bone by bone.*

Breast cancer and any other illness that threatens our life and wellbeing can be a wake up call. It is an opportunity to deal with the pain without denial or dissociation. We can open our eyes and see our world for what it really is. Then we make better choices. Somehow being confronted with one's mortality at a young age can make for a better, more appreciated life from then onwards. It certainly has been the case for me. A colleague in Ireland recently told me a lovely story called The Velveteen Bunny. The story was told as she was leaving her work after many years of counselling with cancer patients. So she related the following story in that light.

There was a toy room where sat a rocking horse and a very worn pre-loved velveteen bunny. The bunny had one eye that was almost falling off, no hair and several stitch lines showing from the many repairs over the years. The rocking horse had heard that under certain circumstances certain toys could become real, so he asked the bunny what one had to do to become real. The bunny answered that all you had to do to become real was to have one damaged eye, no hair and have several stitch lines showing from the many years of wear and tear. Those were the requirements for becoming real.

I was very moved by this little story. Its truth moved the depths of my soul, for so many of the people with cancer who have moved in and out of my life were, at times, velveteen bunnies and yes indeed their illness had made them very real. The question begs however, why do humans so often need adversity in our path to make us real?

Healing the Void

The void can be felt as the sick feeling in the pit of the stomach or the hungry hole that can't be fed enough food or alcohol. There is a hunger in many women today. A hunger that has not been fed and perhaps this is now reflecting to the young women in our society. Like a *shadow* energy, this may be translating into the high incidence of eating disorders in young women. But the real hunger I sense is a spiritual one. Many women are spiritually starving themselves in the name and cause and trying to be everything to everybody. The void cannot be healed by things physical or material. Maybe it is because of our cyclic nature and our connection to nature that we as women need to stay closer to our true selves in order to enjoy real health and wellbeing? Things of the soul can feed our spiritual hunger; things that will reconnect us to ourselves. This is different between men and women. Men, it seems, need to go outwards to find their soul quality and connect with their inner life; for example climbing mountains, sailing the seas, flying the skies, conquering the boardroom. The classic quest! For the feminine, it is different, as the search to connect leads us inwards on a different journey.

The Female–Male Journey:
The Relevance to Healing

The male journey is often taken alone. The female journey is assisted in recovery by being witnessed or empathised with by fellow women. The network of women heals. It is the equivalent of the sewing and quilting circles of old. Both male and female connect with their own soul quality in their own way. This becomes very relevant for partners, carers, your significant other or anyone who chooses to support you on your journey. They will need to do their own journey, whilst supporting yours. Your situation can be a wake up call for them.

Hence the relevance of a support group, counsellor or non-judgmental friend who can listen and empathise with your situation. Sometimes we expect our husbands to fill this role, because they live with us and know us — or at least we think they do. It can save you a lot of frustration if you know and realise that, although love may be there, the male way of helping is "to do", be proactive and find solutions. Whereas what you need is to be acknowledged, heard and understood. Attending a support group for women with breast cancer can be the ideal solution for you to express what you feel and have it understood and empathised with. Some men can do this; but in my experience the majority struggle with the sort of communication that the healing woman needs. This takes the pressure off the relationship and frees up energy to explore other fertile areas together. You can spend a lot of precious time and energy trying to convince your man of your emotional needs and they just won't understand. It is just the way things are!

The Healing Journey

As we tread the path of living true to ourselves, we realise that there are many personal rewards, however the path of self-help and self-discovery is no soft option. It takes courage, determination and an ability to be honest with yourself. As the healing journey begins, we often discover the enormous amount of emotional baggage and the stony repressed silence that is housed within the void. Rather than keep putting a "lid" on these emotions we may need to touch base with them, feel them for a moment and release them. Your practise of deep relaxation and meditation will support you through your emotional healing. It will help you gently unlock emotional doors that have been locked for some time and importantly it will allow you to be gentle with yourself during the process of release. Sometime you might finish a session feeling a little sad or teary. Don't be concerned, this is OK and is a part of the process of gently allowing old feelings and emotions to release. It is not even important to know where they originated and what they were about. Just let them go. Let them go — a process that many women have described to me as like taking a shower on the inside!

Re-awakening the Feminine

This is part of the healing journey for women with breast cancer. With old emotions released and transformed, with day-to-day feelings and emotions experienced rather than held on to, women can really begin to reconnect with their innate and instinctual wisdom. This is a natural consequence when one begins to live true to one's self. With this comes the re-awakening of a deep, inner, feminine power. This power carries with it tremendous healing potential and opens the doorway into intuitive and inner knowing.

You may have begun to experience a sense of the small, still voice within. It is like a deep level of "gut feeling". It is the voice of the inner artist that crafts and shapes the inner world of the feminine. Once you have recognised this voice and become re-acquainted, you may remember that you knew it well as a child. This reconnection with the inner self and an inner life is where the deep healing happens. Some women who have touched this place within and have learned to really know and trust themselves, can be surprised that they need to change little in their outer world. For others choices made for wrong reasons at earlier times in their life may need revaluation. While another group may realise that they are in abusive situations or around people that are toxic to them which will require radical decisions and changes. Be sure that you communicate your needs and that you have the necessary support from friends, family and a counsellor if you need to make radical changes.

You will be aware that so far I have described many aspects of the feminine nature — the female mode of being. I have described how the bottling up of dynamic emotional energy that requires expression leads to fatigue and spells danger to a woman's health.

So now we need to consider how to initiate healing.

The first step in emotional healing is the acknowledgement to yourself of how it has been for you. This may simply involve telling your story, thus bringing your life history to conscious awareness. Journal writing can also work extremely well for those who still find the idea of speaking out to either a group or an individual a little daunting. Most people are amazed to read their life story in this type of format. Telling your story has the power to gently tap into memory and therefore shift and bring movement to stuck emotional patterns. Remember to have the courage to allow expression of any emotions that arise naturally during this process of acknowledgement.

The second step is to recognise that change is required as the way in which you have coped is no longer appropriate. Consider that so far your life is a product of the past. Simply, are you happy with your life now? What is important for you to change to make it better and to provide a healing environment? It seems that for each woman with breast cancer there are issues that revolve around nurturing and relationship. Choose the key events that you recognise as important, as for each woman they will be different and result from individual life experience. No-one can make the changes for you.

The third step is to acknowledge and have respect for the feelings that you have withheld. Remembering that they are a part of you, begin the process of gently and respectfully releasing them. I believe this third process to be highly important in the healing process. For women, putting a lid of positive thinking principles on top of unrecognised, ignored or unreleased emotions is not being honest with yourself. Healing requires that we are honest with ourselves. Allow yourself the luxury to bottom out for a day or two. Throughout the entire process of your healing give yourself time out and the luxury of a low energy day every now and then. Some people have a misconception that healing is about being warm and sunny all the time. It is not. It is about being real, honest and true to yourself.

Summary of the Steps on the Healing Journey:

1. Acknowledging the real issues.
2. Recognition that changes are required.
3. Respectfully and gently releasing emotion.
4. Being honest with yourself.
5. Applying the skills and tools to allow healing.
6. Approaching healing with heart and passion.

Being Open to Healing

Like people, healing can come in many diverse and different packages. Opening yourself to new ideas and understandings is also a part of the journey. For example many steps on the path of our journey are completely foreign. We are continually confronted with new ideas and concepts. The majority of them lead us somewhere or to someone who is useful. There are also some that are completely and utterly "red herrings" but at least we need to check their validity and know that they are not suitable. Sometimes during the re-awakening process women will return to a discarded religion or spiritual practice that may now be viewed with the maturity of the years and the value of hindsight. My only suggestion here is that you don't lose your powers of discrimination. Healthy scepticism and openness are fine partners. If in doubt, be still, listen and follow your gut feel. It is usually right.

Re-engaging Your Passion

What is your *raison d'être*? What motivates you to find healing? Where *did* you stop singing, dancing and being comfortable with your life story? The answers to these questions are just as important as deciding what type of chemotherapy or other treatments you will have. This section of the healing pie chart is yours and only yours. Remember too that this responsibility is not about you having caused your cancer. The illness is an opportunity to add value to your life and encourage self-discovery. There is no trade off. By saying that I mean to clarify that, just because you do these things, it doesn't necessarily mean that you have found an antidote that will equalise out your life like a list of ticks and crosses. But my thirty year long experience in this field tells me that you will increase health, wellbeing and treatment response and your life will be much better if you pay attention to your emotional healing.

Rather than taking the view that the previous questions are just another thing to do, why not reframe them for yourself. See the healing as an adventure, a journey of discovery and a way of learning to be intimate with yourself. The focus then is not so intensely driven towards killing the cancer, but rather towards healing the self. This is a win–win situation.

Re-engaging your passion can be fun and healing too. What is it that has stopped you enjoying a passion in your life? What can you do to re-engage with that passion?

The Story of Carla

Carla had been an opera singer. It was her life and her love. In her mid-twenties she met, fell in love with and married a man who was also in the music world. He was pianist and a pedantic perfectionist. Although she was also a perfectionist she liked to bend the rules by adding more feeling and emotion into her singing. According to him she was technically incorrect. Rather than work on the stage they created a business singing at functions and in classy hotels. People loved her creative style but the fact that he could not adapt to her technical incorrectness became the subject of the battleground of their marriage. In front of the audience there were accolades and behind the scenes there were heated arguments. Despite the ongoing issues, Carla loved this man. Eventually she stopped singing and he continued as a soloist. She described the feeling within herself as if a beautiful red rose inside of her had faded and then withered. She had begun to over eat and had difficulty conceiving children and eventually gave up trying. Not surprisingly her relationship failed when she discovered her husband was having an affair with another singer whom she had introduced to him. Feeling angry and betrayed she pursued many other relationships looking for the "fix", the something that would bring her to life again. It was only when she had a diagnosis of inflammatory breast cancer when in her forties that she took stock of her life and began once more to sing. This re-engagement with her passion proved to be an appropriate adjunct to her medical treatment. Singing again was the only change that she made to her life, as well as an understanding that she would never walk again in the shoes of another at the expense of losing her passion.

How to Re-engage Your Passion

1. Identify key times in your past when you really enjoyed a particular hobby, vocation, past-time.
2. Identify why you stopped this particular activity.
3. If you can't go back to exactly that activity, how could you modify it so that you could partake once more.
4. Search out resources and information.
5. Make a decision and plan the time that you would like to spend with this activity.
6. Do it! Enjoy it!

Just One Thing

Like Carla some women with breast cancer will be able to identify just one thing that they "know inside of themselves" that will make a difference. Also, for some, changing just one major thing leads on to making changes to smaller facets of your life. Healing does not have to be complicated or confusing — it is us that make it so. The "fix-it" mentality in healing can sometimes cloud the way with too many options and too many things to take and do. We have forgotten how to be balanced people and have become too dependent upon external remedies. The external remedies may help us whether they originate from alternative or orthodox remedies. But you know, in retrospect, I have probably learned the most that is of real value from those that have been dying. It is at that point in time when you realise exactly what *is* important and what *was* important in your life. What you will take with you at your death is not to be found in a bottle or a vial. That is why I give priority to the various levels of our existence that at the literal end of the day will dictate your quality of death.

The Role of Women of Wisdom

If you are one of the strong, gentle and silent women with breast cancer seeking wise counsel, support and nurturing, the appearance of wise and understanding women in your life will be a blessing. These women can help you to revive your creative life, show you the way with a gentle and guiding hand and help you to reconnect with your inner self. They are women who are initiated into life and know how to keep the balance of the two worlds — the intellect and the intuition. You may be surprised where you can find them! Usually, they are of the world, initiated by the fires of life and forged into tempered steel; yet strangely they also have a softness.

Seek the company of such women on your healing journey, for they will help you to speak your truth. They are survivors themselves who can teach you how to deal creatively with major life issues. It may be that your natural mother is the one with whom you need to connect, but more than likely it will be strangers who fill the role, even if your relationship with your mother is a happy and loving one.

For regular support I recommend also that you seek the company of a women's circle. Such circles are once again rising in popularity as women recognise the importance of sisterly bonding in their lives and understand their feminine nature and needs. Basically, women need women with whom they can communicate, trust, and share the experience of living a passionate life.

Also, it will be very helpful to find out where your nearest Cancer Support Group operates from and attend regularly. At such venues you are likely to meet other women going through similar experiences to yourself and also women — wise women — who have walked the path of cancer and survived.

Humour

Humour is an essential part of emotional healing. Don't forget to look for humour in life, in movies, in what you read. When my ex and I began our healing journey, we became so engrossed in techniques, methods, regimes, juices and enemas that we simply forgot to laugh and enjoy ourselves along the way. We forgot that humour is therapeutic! Science even tells us now that humour heals. Apart from Patch Adams, the other well known person who specifically used humour in his recovery was Norman Cousins. His books *Anatomy of an Illness* (and the video of the same name) and *The Healing Heart*, although now dated, are worth reading.

Norman was diagnosed with a supposedly incurable and very painful disease called ankylosing spondylitis. It is particularly interesting that his self-prescribed laughter therapy that was helped by watching Marx Brothers movies in the hospital, substantially reduced his pain.

Look for humour in your life. Self-prescribe a comedy video each day as a part of your healing program. Buy a joke book. Laugh it up! You may be surprised at how good it feels.

Chapter Seven

The Healing Power of Story

The wisdom of the Storyteller is the art of remembering.
The wisdom of the story is the image or the symbol.
The result is the healing.

The most helpful initial intervention for a woman dealing with breast cancer is to provide her with the opportunity and the space to tell her own story. Indeed for any woman who recognises the need to move forward in life but feels "stuck" or inhibited by the past, the telling of your life story can be a truly liberating experience. In fact even writing your story is helpful. Some years ago a prospective residential participant, wrote to me stating that she could not possibly tell her story in front of a group of people. Instead she wrote her story, all ten pages of it and posted it to me prior to attending. This process began a chain reaction of healing events and although she had already written her story, she bravely vocalised the issues to the group.

The externalising of one's life experience in story allows for a personal review. With this comes a re-orientation of your position and place in life, as well as an acknowledgement of the past. Story is also a natural and gentle way of accessing memory and its associated emotions in a non-threatening way. Take a moment to consider how your personal history, your story or past is affecting your current life. Your perceptions, actions and reactions to life are all coloured by your past. This will be so whether that past has been a basically happy one or a life of traumatic events that has stripped you of passion and enthusiasm.

One quality of survivors who tell their story, is that they can speak of their experience, no matter how traumatic it was, with a focus on the lessons they learned in facing the major challenge in their life. They can speak with authority about their survival, look for the good in all experiences and talk of how they have come through with new abilities and strengths that had never been used or recognised before.

With the natural healing that time allows, the survivor's story changes in form and content as a part of the process of integration and healing. From time-to-time in our groups we had many survivors of POW camps from the second world war who were now dealing with a threat of another kind — cancer. Their often courageous stories, humbly recounted and told with great feeling, have provided precious insights into the mechanisms of survival. One hero or survivor coming along and sharing their story can provide a wealth of useful information, but more important is the hope and inspiration that the power of their story can generate. Such stories demonstrate the power of the human spirit. The ability of survivors not to be victims, but to thrive in whatever circumstances with dignity and self-assurance, show true qualities of soul-force or spirit in action. I suggest that you read as many inspiring stories of this nature as you can, for we all have the survivor quality within us to varying degrees just waiting to be awoken (e.g. see *Women of Silence: Pearls of Wisdom*). Choose to watch videos or DVDs that have inspiring stories that can enrich your knowledge base and fire up your enthusiasm.

When our inner life is paralysed by emotions such as fear and anxiety, the power of story can cut a path directly through, causing movement of the mysterious energies within. A story told well and from the heart provokes the imagination, igniting the fire, the magic and the mystery. Story relates to and connects us with our fellow human beings. This is a limbic brain activity, the part of the brain associated with healing. The joy of story is that the process can bring about transformations in a non-threatening and non-judgemental manner. For the storyteller or writer remains impersonal, like silent teachers whose blackboard is the psyche and whose chalks are the vibrant colours of the soul. Such storytellers are creating the inner landscapes of image.

Story and image bring a sense of aliveness and inner connectedness to healing. Importantly for the woman with breast cancer, when those stories are authentic, they become like beacons of hope in the stormy sea of life.

The Function of Stories in Cancer Support Groups

Imagine a room filled with twenty people all around forty years of age; some of them Italian, some Jewish, Indian, Australian and British. Think of their diverse backgrounds with different cultures, belief systems, religions, social interactions, dietary habits and so on. How could there be one approach or system that could deal with such a diverse range of past experience? In an effective support group, however, they would all have an opportunity to tell their story to listening ears so that an understanding would evolve of how they have come to be in their present life circumstances. Sometimes during the telling of these stories heads would nod as other people in the group catch glimpses of their own life journey passing before them. There is relevance in acknowledging the past. It is like following a detailed map that shows you how you arrived at your destination. This information then provides you with a direction, an indication of how you might make the rest of the journey.

Some may require the assistance of a counsellor but often the collective wisdom of the group will provide a safety net of wisdom to support and understand their pain and their story. If we take the example of the group above, just consider the collective amount of "wisdom years" in the room — twenty people times forty years equals eight hundred collective years of life experience and wisdom! It is the equivalent of an eight hundred year old counsellor! It is extraordinary how often this collective wisdom is sufficient, in that it helps to provide a safe space into which people can expand and tell their story as if they are the most important people in the world. Stories told by women in other countries where the command of the English language is average are recounted so succinctly and so eloquently. One of the distinct advantages of taking my workshops worldwide has been that it has given me an insight into cross-cultural emotional issues. It has shown me that as women, we have universal emotional issues that are remarkably similar.

Isolated events that on their own would be impressive to listen to, are often only small segments of the whole story of someone's life. Sometimes the stories are recounted in detail; other times they are merely fleeting feelings and wispy memories of events too painful to remember in detail. However, once expression begins, these events are brought to conscious awareness and the process of healing can begin. Emotion will move as the story touches upon the unhealed, no matter how old the wound is.

What stays in the deep, dark cavern of the psyche cannot have access to the light of healing, hence the importance of expression and communication in relevance to recovery.

A personal story at this point will provide an understanding of this from the patient's point of view.

Debbie's Story

"Two years after a mastectomy I am feeling better than I have ever felt in my life. For the first time I am at peace. No moment in the day is taken for granted. I am happy to live my life. I am aware it is a gift. I attended a self-help programme six months after my operation. It took the best part of two years to recover from the shock and at the time of the programme I was still feeling fragile. I was not sure that I wanted to go into a situation where I would be surrounded by people who are ill. But the experience was quite the contrary. The feeling was positive and friendly.

People became very close and experienced friendship in a way that they had never known before. I shall never forget the warmth and love, the stories we shared and the inspiration, and the feeling of wellbeing that this brought."

Stories that Heal

The power of stories to heal has been recognised and practised by healers and shamans of all cultures for thousands of years. Some cultures today still hold sacred their art of storytelling. For them it is a way of life, a way of passing on to younger generations the tribal wisdom that has been gathered. Also in tribal cultures, myths and story are used to reinforce social behaviour and the belief systems that are an integral part of the structure and survival of the people.

Unfortunately, many modern cultures have dispensed stories into the realm of children's learning and entertainment. But have you ever noticed how adults really enjoy themselves when reading classic fairytales or adventure stories to young children? There is a simplicity in these stories and yet their symbols and messages can be quite profound. We all tend to remember the stories that touched us deeply in childhood and when we read them to a child it is always fascinating to see how they bring memories flooding back. These stories are metaphors for our life in current time.

Remember the biblical quote regarding healing:

"In order to heal ye must be as little children."

Also, cast your mind back to the third question in the cross-cultural questions mentioned earlier:

"Where in your life did you become uncomfortable with story, particularly the sound of your own life story?"

When on the time line of your life did you lose enchantment? When did you lose heart and soul or passion for your life and can the story help you to reclaim the lost pieces?

Stories can take us back to that state of uncluttered mind where healing images can simply communicate their messages. Some stories are archetypal in nature, with powerful messages carried in words, symbols and images. These stories reach to places within, that would otherwise be inaccessible. Fairytales, fables and parables are certainly in this realm. This is why today many people are reviving the "story" within their cultural heritage. They are reconnecting with a power that enables survival and they are reinforcing their spiritual belief systems. The Women's Movement and the Men's Movement are both using the power of story to reconnect with the precious lineage of the feminine and the masculine.

Stories, by way of their ability to gain access into the inner psyche, can act as catalysts to initiate change. Images and symbols are the language of this realm and although healing requires the use of both masculine and feminine qualities, it seems that women often have a more immediate and direct connection with the use of story and imagery. This is probably due to the fact that women are seen to have a predominance of so-called right (limbic) brain function which is the intuitive and creative part of the brain. Men can find it difficult if they do not easily have access to creativity in their life but it is a skill which can be learnt. Life is an act of constantly balancing our feminine forces of creativity with the masculine forces of will. Often there is a struggle and a resulting inner chaos if we get these principles out of balance for any long period of time.

For instance, a working mother who is a business executive may find that to survive in a male environment she must use will, decisiveness and aggression in order to be competitive with her peers. This can cause a woman all sorts of problems as a result of her nurturing and intuitive side being forced into the background. I have seen this pattern in many younger women dealing with breast cancer. When the first **Women of Silence** was published, the prestigious Australian magazine, *The Bulletin*, was the first to review it. Understandably my first groups over many months were almost all corporate women with breast cancer. This enabled me to gain some significant insights into the issues of women who struggle to climb the corporate ladder of success — often at great expense to their health and wellbeing. You can see that although their story is different to those of other women we have spoken of, the key issue still centres on misdirected nurturing. These women are often highly stressed and out of adrenaline. They are often suffering from complete exhaustion and fatigue. Usually they have been operating under immense pressure and their suffering is of an intense and silent nature. But, once diagnosed, having the pattern of being the doers and achievers in life, they are usually highly self-motivated and enthusiastically embrace creative healing techniques. Recovery for these women essentially requires time out to balance their outer life with their inner life. For these women too, the use of stories that relate to the recovery of the feminine can be very helpful.

Two Tales of Transformational Healing

Reclaiming your soul skin

The story that I am about to share with you was passed on, as stories are, by a female Irish storyteller. Interestingly you will find a similar story told in the oral tradition by many of the world's indigenous peoples.

Long, long ago in the days when the people of Ireland lived a simple life dependent upon the fruits that the sea brought them, there began a legend. The legend of the mermaid seal. Now these were the days when the island people lived close to the shore in tidy whitewashed cottages with roofs made of peat and thatch. The people were fair of skin and hair but occasionally a "dark one" was born who had eyes as deep as the sea and more brown than the earth on which they stood.

The old ones tell that long ago a young fisherman named Liam was going about his daily catch when he took his boat to shore to rest a while. He walked along the rocky beach seeking shelter from the wind when he came across a sleek brown seal resting within the crevice of a rocky outcrop. The seal had not seen him and so he sat and watched the creature stretching and basking in the afternoon sun. He sat still, silent and mesmerised at what began to unfold before his very eyes. The slippery brown creature of the deep slowly began to stretch, turning her body from side to side in order to shed her furry pelt as one would expect of a butterfly abandoning its cocoon. Webbed flippers transformed into long slender fingers and the furry pelt was now replaced by skin, pink and tender. Long wavy locks of dark brown hair now encircled a face more beautiful than Liam had ever seen. Liam could not believe his eyes at the transformation before him. Being discreet not to be seen he crawled nearer to the young woman who lay naked upon the rocks drying herself and enjoying the last of the afternoon sun. Liam noticed that her seal-skin was now at some distance from the lovely creature. He was totally seduced by her beauty, her freedom, her spirit, her seal-ness.

There had been many tales of the sea told by the old ones of mermaids who guided ships in times of trouble and then disappeared among the seals. The seal therefore gained a reputation in myth as a creature of the feminine. Liam awaited his opportunity to surprise the creature and upon impulse he first leapt onto the rocks and secured the lank damp brown pelt so that she could not slip away from him and home to the sea. For some time they looked at each other totally seduced by the moment. Then with her seal-skin tucked firmly under his arm, he covered her naked body with his jacket. Without murmuring a word he led her to his boat and took her back across the waters to his people who lived on a nearby island. As he rowed the boat into shore, the women gathered on the sand. The girl was obviously out of place and the old women in particular gossiped, clustered in small groups, for they knew where the dark girl had come from. She spoke an ancient tongue not heard of for many centuries and so began her new life. She endured great loneliness and longing and would stand for many hours knee deep in the water looking out to sea. Liam made the young woman his wife. She worked hard and she bore him many children who grew fine and strong.

Many years had passed and she was now approaching the middle time of her life. The longing had grown deep in her; but although she searched her heart and soul often, she could not know what it was that she was longing for. But one day while collecting cockles on the beach with her children the eldest of them asked: "Mother who is the owner of the dark brown seal coat that father keeps hidden in the attic?" At that moment, she knew. She remembered. The sea beckoned her in a silent and secret language. She dropped the basket of cockles, ran into the house and climbed the small stairs that led to the attic. There in a corner, bound tightly with rope was her skin, her seal skin, her soul skin. Carrying the skin and without a word to her children she walked into the sea until she disappeared from sight. When Liam came home that night he was devastated but understood that she had gone back from whence she came.

From that time on, everyday, a large brown furry seal with eyes as deep as the sea and more brown than the earth on which they stood came in to the shallows. It was as if she were keeping a watchful eye upon the children. She had her freedom once again, for as much as she loved Liam and her children, the price of seduction had been high and she now grieved the fact that she had lost her options to move between the two worlds. Covered again by her soul skin and wiser for the experience, she remained a presence around the island for many years.

For many generations and only on occasion, the blood of the young seal woman would rise up again and thus would be born a "dark one" who innately knew of the mysteries of the sea and the importance of caring for the soul skin.

As women we nurture and give to our families so easily but often forget the self and the self-care that is our birthright. So often, young and naïve, we are seduced by young men, themselves also immature who also have lost their soul skin.

Together we try to make a go of this thing called relationship and marriage. The more we move away from nature, the more we move away from the contact with our essence or soul. T'is a pity that it is often the menopausal years that allow us to wear our soul-skin for all to see. For men it is the mid-life or mid-career crisis that can provide this privileged opportunity. It is always a choice, a conscious choice to stay in longing, emptiness or loneliness, for what we are all looking for is our sense of belonging. To find this sense of belonging first and foremost, for and within yourself, is paramount before you go looking for it in an-other. To reclaim your magic and slip on your soul skin, making it a good fit and living true to self, is the gift that a life brings.

Suffering, healing, change and forgiveness are the lessons of the following Moroccan Tale, known as a lesson story.

The stoning

Once upon a time, a husband left his wife and home to go on a pilgrimage, as was the custom of their people. Before he departed the man went to his brother, who was a judge, and asked him to look after his wife.

"Gladly", said the brother. As soon as the husband left, the judge went to the wife. "This is my chance!" he thought, because he had long coveted his brother's wife. The judge brought a gift with him and knocked at the door. The wife was no fool; she knew what her brother-in-law wanted and turned him away.

Undaunted, the judge returned the next day with an even more costly gift. But the wife only scolded him. "What are you doing?" she exclaimed. "I am your brother's wife. Have you no shame?"

Angered by her words, the judge went to his court. Before the whole village he accused his sister-in-law of being a prostitute. The judge was an elegant speaker, and his words inflamed everyone. The people stormed the wife's house, dragged the innocent woman out, and threw stones at her until she collapsed. Then the villagers left her for dead.

A little later, a traveller passed by the pile of stones and heard moaning from within. He dug through the rocks and found the wife, barely breathing. The traveller took pity on her and carried her home to his own wife and family. The kind man and his wife nursed the injured woman back to health and invited her to stay with them.

When the wounded wife recovered, she found that she could heal the sick. She cured a neighbour's fever and gave sight back to a blind man. Word of her power spread throughout the land, and people came to her for their ailments. So the wife began a new life as a healer. Everyday she received the sick from behind a screen, hidden from view, and asked questions of her patients. Then she advised them on a cure, and all who came to her went away healed.

Meanwhile far away in his village, the judge succumbed to a grave illness. Ugly sores spread over his body and festered painfully. He summoned doctors and priests, but they could not cure him. The judge tried potions and lotions, and he prayed at all the holy places. But nothing worked. Day by day he grew weaker and more hideous.

The judge's brother finally returned from his pilgrimage. He found his house empty and hurried to his brother. "Where is my wife?" he exclaimed.

"She was stoned to death for being a prostitute!" the judge explained.

"What are you talking about?" the husband demanded. He could not believe his ears. But the judge and the villagers repeated the story.

"She is dead." the judge said. The husband was heartbroken, but there was nothing he could do. Then he noticed how ill his brother was. "On my travels", the husband said "I heard of a great healer who lives some distance from here. People say she can cure anybody. Let us go to her and see if she can heal you."

The judge agreed, and they set off together. When they arrived, the woman healer saw that the two men were her husband and his brother. But they did not recognise her because she sat behind her screen.

"Tell me about your illness", the wife asked, disguising her voice. The judge recounted his miseries and the remedies he had tried.

"The cause of this malady", the wife declared, "is a grave sin you have committed. Confess this crime, or you cannot recover."

The sick man said, "I am a judge! I have committed no wrong!"

The wife repeated, "Confess your sin, or you cannot be healed."

"I am innocent", the judge insisted.

The husband spoke up. "Brother, whatever it is, confess! Otherwise you will die from your horrible illness!"

Finally the judged stirred. Weeping with shame and remorse, he told his brother, "I coveted your wife, and when she rebuffed me, I accused her falsely of being a prostitute. So the villagers stoned her to death."

With those words, the wife drew aside the screen and stepped forward. The husband was amazed to see her. Then he ran to embrace her. The wife said, "I will cure your brother if you desire it."

The husband thought a moment and nodded. "My brother has suffered enough, and he has repented. Cure him if you can."

The wife went to the judge and healed him. His sores vanished, and he stood up from his stretcher. The wife and husband returned home in great happiness, while the judge followed behind — chastened and changed.

"The Stoning" can give us profound insights into the nature of illness, recovery and transformation. Stories of this nature have been handed down over centuries and symbolize the reality of traumatic life encounters as well as providing the remedy, the healing and the lesson.

The wife in the story has been treated unfairly, first by being wrongly accused and then by being stoned. This symbolizes the "wounding", which no doubt is added to by the betrayal of the villagers. She is buried under a pile of stones and left for dead. She then dies the symbolic death (classically talked about in healing circles as the Shaman's death — a time when the old way of life ceases and a totally new way begins). She is found by a traveller and offered care and compassion. When she recovers, she has the power to heal the sick (transformation of the wounded healer). She then seeks to have her truth known and through transcendence and compassion, (the initiated wise woman) grants forgiveness and healing to the judge.

In relation to the journey of a woman with breast cancer, similar stages are passed through.

Stages of the Emotional Healing of Breast Cancer

1. Emotional "wounding".
2. Emotional and physical suffering.
3. Symbolic death.
4. Transformational healing.
5. Initiation into the "wounded" healer: The *scar clan*.
6. Wise woman: Giving healing, compassion and forgiveness, leading to revitalisation and renewal for all.

I see these principles so often in my work. A woman who heals her breast cancer, having travelled through the dark tunnel of uncertainty herself, heals her life, heals her "wound" and becomes the one who can point the way for others.

Selecting Stories

When selecting stories for healing, allow your intuition to guide you. You will know instantly when a story is relevant for *you*. It will touch a place deep within. You will be aware of a movement, a resonance within your being that brings an immediate recognition. In that moment you will know what needs paying attention to.

Sometimes stories appropriate to your need or your illness will be replicated, or appear symbolically during your sleeping dreams. Be grateful for them if they do for they will surely have significance for you.

Remember too, that stories are not given to us by The Storyteller from the village any more, but are more likely to be presented to us in ready made images such as in film and television. According to some American studies that were conducted a few years ago, the powerful images of film can affect the functioning and status of our immune system.

Immunological tests were conducted before and after viewing of the films and followed up for a period of one month. Two films were used in the study, one a light and happy film and the other a horror film. Researchers found that the effects of the happy movie gave significant increases in immune function. However, the horror movie group saw corresponding, significant negative decreases in their immunity.

I would suggest that "feel good" movies are a wise choice. Use the power of story to every advantage and as with literature, choose positive reading that will inspire and amuse rather than depress you.

I will leave you with an old Hasidic proverb that tells us something of the power of story to heal.

"Give people a fact or an idea; and you enlighten their minds; Give people a story and you touch their souls!"

Chapter Eight

Post Traumatic Stress Disorder

(PTSD is the abbreviation used in this chapter)

The Absence of Presence

When people are in trauma they will often describe a sense of unreality about their life, a feeling of being *beside themselves, disconnected, out of it, numbed out* or as one patient said, it is like functioning on *automatic pilot*. This sense of separation is also known as dissociation and it has been a part of almost every life story that I have listened to. When this occurs, a person's boundaries are affected in a way that does not serve them. Either they become vulnerable and lose their sense of self, merging easily into the boundaries of others or they build boundaries that act as impenetrable walls to try to protect themselves. At times the wall is up and they can screen out life and at other times the wall is absent, leaving them open and vulnerable to life and situations.

This absence of presence, in other words, not being present in the here and now is, I believe, a pivotal issue for attention and one of the first steps on the path to healing and recovery. Cross-cultural wisdom tells us that *"in order to heal you need to be present"*. Tibetans tell us that true meditation is about bringing the mind home — that is to become present to your life. For some years my private practice was called *Ellimatta* which is a Wurrundjeri word meaning "returning home". Because when people become present again to life they are indeed returning home to the self. They become empowered and resilient. This is *the key* to living well. I name that process *healing*.

90

I believe that this process often happens via touch, the laying on of hands and other spiritual practices, as well as by the spoken word. If a traumatic event is too tragic to voice; the use of touch by a healer who is *present* (*who is living in the moment*) can be the catalyst to bring home the spirit and thus begins the process of re-integration. From that point on, the soul, the person, is on the road to recovery.

The lack of recognition of the effects of the trauma of diagnosis, the trauma of the life before diagnosis, the trauma of treatments and the uncertainty of outcome have attracted little attention over the years. This has not only been in breast cancer; I have observed this PTSD pattern as a matter of course in many chronic illnesses and conditions. Despite the large body of research and web sites verifying the existence of PTSD, its clinical application has somewhat lagged behind. Recent world events in America have brought home the fact that trauma has a deep impact on the human psyche.

The lack of application of this information to illness is a missing link in both mainstream and alternative cancer care. My experience has been that by naming this condition and then explaining its symptoms and solutions, a great deal of anxiety and concern has been alleviated for many women. You see as well as the cancer experience a woman is also experiencing PTSD and its symptoms. This combination can make it difficult to decipher which symptoms are due to PTSD and which are due to treatment. If PTSD is identified and the process of dealing with it is begun, all treatments whether orthodox medical treatments, complementary or alternative, will be invariably more effective. My own anecdotal research has implied that recurrence rate might be significantly reduced if therapeutic measures were instigated for dealing with effects of PTSD closer to the time of diagnosis. In 1998 the *Medical Journal of Australia* published a research article by David Kissane et al entitled "*Psychological morbidity and quality of life in Australian women with early stage breast cancer: a cross sectional survey*". The conclusion of this study is one to be actively taken to heart by all clinicians:

"Conclusion: Women diagnosed with early stage breast cancer have high rates of psychiatric and psychological disturbance. Quality of life is substantially affected. Clinicians should actively explore their patients' psychological adjustment to enable early recognition and treatment of these disorders." The application for this information in oncology is obvious.

PTSD is a condition resulting from one trauma or enduring chronic exposure to trauma. There is usually some kind of threat involved with survival, either a death, or a threat of death or injury. This can be related to self or others. Trauma is experienced differently by everyone, due to genetic make up and people's general vulnerability to pressure. Hormonal problems can also be a part of the onset of PTSD as can chronic emotional and psychological pressure.

The symptoms of PTSD included:

- Depression, anxiety, insomnia.
- Decline or absence of *joie de vivre*.
- A feeling of being removed from those around you.
- A feeling of being numb or frozen.
- Dreams/memories/flashbacks that return, where the trauma is relived repeatedly or intermittently.
- A feeling of being drained — emotionally flat and unresponsive.
- Avoidance of situations/people.
- Emotional outbursts — panic, aggression, fear, and over excitability — can be dramatic.
- Addictions of all types.

When we look at these symptoms, I am again reminded of the life stories of my clients especially those who are dealing with breast cancer or other chronic illness.

Surprisingly, even surviving cancer, can be for some people, a source of psychological, emotional and spiritual issues to be dealt with. Not only is this related to living with *life-altering illness*; but also can be associated with the *guilt* of having survived. Many recovered patients have told me that they have felt very guilty and awkward when attending funerals of other group members who had died as a result of their cancer. In this case, instead of the *why me?* as a cause it becomes the *why me as a survivor? Why am I alive?*

Partners and supporters of people who are dealing with a life-threatening, chronic illness or an acquired life-changing condition can also experience PTSD. This very often goes undiagnosed and may be one of the reasons for the high death rate of spouses of people who have died from cancer who do not grieve or seek counselling. The time lapse post death is often around two years.

In relation to cancer, a diagnosis of cancer is the result of a series of traumas. It is not just one traumatic event. The consequences of trauma can arise at any time throughout your treatment or life after cancer. Life's traumas often cannot be avoided. If we need to have a treatment intervention that is not pleasant, but essential, how can we best manage to go through it with a spiritual edge, a resilience that supports us so that we experience as little effect of the trauma as possible? The solution can be just a few sessions with a counsellor, psychologist or psychotherapist. Support groups also work well particularly as a follow on. Extreme cases may require the advice of a psychiatrist or even the prescribing of antidepressants or the like. If this is not acknowledged and is left unattended the trauma of further treatments will be amplified.

In some countries, such as the United Kingdom, there are enormous strains on the National Health System (NHS) and long waiting times from diagnosis to treatment or surgery. An opportunity is therefore provided for patients to take advantage of psychological counselling or psychotherapeutic methods to deal with PTSD. However that being said, one of my UK clients in need of help for trauma was on a waiting list for more than three months to see a counsellor under the NHS system. Fortunately she was in a financial position to be able to seek private counselling.

PTSD can be more often identified by someone else, a clinician or partner for instance. Often PTSD is not recognised by the person who is experiencing it yet paradoxically they know that they feel removed from reality. They may presume their symptoms are more a result of their treatments. Evaluation of PTSD can be a challenge when there are so many issues going on in a person's life, but from my experience for anyone dealing with chronic illness dealing with PTSD is the first port of call.

Sensitivity to Patient Needs and PTSD

One area that requires a very special sensitivity, particularly in the clinical or diagnostic situation, is a patient's historical background in relation to lack of control, victimisation or abuse. Some years ago after presenting a women's lecture for Jewish Passover, I acquired many holocaust survivors and children of holocaust survivors in my practice. This was a humbling education for me — and a challenge. The one issue that came to my attention was the association between many of the diagnostic and treatment procedures and those re-visited past traumatic memories of the concentration camps. These individual cases, on grounds of compassion, need special attention. If you are a holocaust survivor, first and second generation, or a survivor of abuse, please identify this to your clinician and ask for the services of an in-house counsellor if you are to undergo any invasive tests. Don't just sit with the fear.

Addictions and PTSD

Alexa was an imposing woman, although wiry in stature. The deeply etched lines on her gaunt face told the story of a woman who had survived much hardship with little or no self-care. Her feeling of self-esteem was rock bottom after several failed marriages; she was now in a relationship with a much older man for whom she felt no love. The removal of her left breast due to breast cancer had added to the tension in the marriage. Her prognosis was not good and she knew that changes were required, but her lack of financial independence kept her anchored in a joyless life. A more naïve group member asked her how she could tolerate the situation. With a wry smile she turned to the woman and with her thick Russian accent said: *"Dalink, I just have six whiskeys before he comes home and I can tolerate anything!"*

This was not the first time that I had heard stories of all kinds of substance abuse from the traumatised women in my groups. Alexa was at a choice point in her healing. She took on board some of my suggestions; however she consciously chose to stay "stuck" in what she knew. Much of her life had been lived unconsciously; on automatic pilot for survival and this had become her habitual way of life. Her trauma, combined with the alcohol, removed her from a life she did not want to be living. These were long term survival strategies that she had developed and now that she had at least told her story to someone, that was enough. She died six months later.

I was interested to see in the research article by David Kissane et al (quoted earlier), that their findings were that 20% of the women in the survey had two or more psychiatric issues, with nicotine dependence the commonest second diagnosis. Addictions can also include the addiction to perfection, obsessive–compulsive disorder and workaholic tendencies. If you see yourself in this pattern, give your inner pain a voice and seek help.

Finally, in studying survivors of bone cancer and Hodgkin's lymphoma, the time between diagnosis and treatment has been shown to cause PTSD. It should therefore be a recommended intervention alongside any other treatments offered or in the gap period awaiting treatment.

Basically, I believe that the world of medicine and healing needs more people trained in the psycho-social interventions, with more life coaches for cancer patients. Accordingly I believe that the load taken from the public health purse would have a major impact on health spending. It is not easy when dealing with enormous populations, however it is pleasing to see one self motivated solution being the public swell of self-help groups developing around the globe. People need people and people need to connect. Our isolation in the twenty-first century is the result of breaking down the bonds of humanity as an expense of progress. We need to educate our communities so that treatment of disease is reduced, by addressing lifestyle issues, diet, relationships and emotional health! Our spiritual health has declined. This is just as important in the holistic health model as a society.

Chapter Nine

The Anatomy of Stress

How we view the world will determine very much how we understand stress. An event that is stressful to one person may be a positive challenge to another. Stress is now defined as "active" stress and "passive" stress. Active stress is a motivating experience, a healthy part of getting things done. A recent study used saliva samples taken from thirty male volunteers who were placed in various stressful situations. The results were that active stress actually boosted the immune system. Using a measurement for levels of secretor proteins, the ones that protect against the invasion of bacteria, they also ascertained that the levels decreased during passive stress. Passive stress can be encountered in everyday events; the type of stress that one can enjoy, yet be removed from, for instance, watching a movie. Passive stress in real life however can build up without us being conscious of it. This is where coping comes into the picture. We learn to cope with this type of stress but one day we experience "the straw that breaks the camel's back". From the poem: *Too much held too often has taken its toll*". When a stressful situation is prolonged or unresolved, termed "passively endured" and you feel "stuck", or that there is nothing that you can do about it but just endure, health problems may be close on the horizon.

This may explain why when people retire or even go on a longed for vacation, they become ill. Having almost become dependent on the buzz, the drive, in the competitive world — their ability to switch off is very compromised. It seems that one of the problems is that with constant stress a person never really experiences what relaxation is like because the adrenaline buzz is always there. We know that this constant state of alert boosts the performance of the immune response; but if this goes on for too long it equals depletion, the condition known as burnout.

As early as the seventies, a group of researchers were gathering results of the effect of grief and bereavement on the immune system. They found that shock, the emotional pain of loss and a lack of the ability to cope with the profound life-change that sudden bereavement brings, all contribute to a significant drop in immune function. The parts of the immune system which attacks foreign invaders and cancer cells, known as T cells, were seen to be significantly lower in bereaved people two months after the bereavement. Some patients in this study took up to fourteen months to recover full immune function again. Importantly this study was done with patients who were offered services of bereavement counsellors. What is it like for people who have no counselling support at all?

To date, there exist tens of thousands of scientific studies that have shown significant results regarding the impact of prolonged stress on the human body. The science known as pyscho-neuro-immunology is the study of the pathways or connections between the mind, emotion, the nervous systems, the hormones and the immune system. There have been very exciting developments in this field that give credence to the anecdotal results obtained by therapists who work with attitudinal and behavioural healing and holistic therapies in general.

In particular if we consider breast cancer, with its predominance of hormonal issues, we now know that there is direct cellular communication to the receptors of oestrogens, progestins and other hormones. Messages from the brain, via the receptors, to the cell provide directions as to the cell's task. So when you change your attitude, you are communicating with your body, and in so doing, over a period of time, you can change your immune chemistry or hormonal status! The immune system, brain and gastrointestinal tract accommodate some two hundred neuropeptides or messenger molecules. The endorphin response experienced in pain relief and some meditation states is a neuropeptide experience where the brain produces its own morphine. Neuropeptides communicate at a distance using the receptors on cells creating what some have termed a "psychosomatic communication network". It is like a superhighway of communication, a network link that takes messages between brain, thought, emotions and body.

Basically this new understanding tells us that the brain "talks" to the immune system and other parts of the body and vice versa. It is a double feedback system. This intricate system of cellular communication links the effects of our way of life to the chemistry of our body. Our thoughts, beliefs, attitudes, emotions and stress responses all contribute to the overall result be it health or disease. Combined with genetics, conditioning, diet and the myriad of other influences, we now understand that the pathways that lead to illness are multi-factorial but that there is one trigger factor activated on the end of a long line of causes that produces the illness. That trigger factor is usually stress related.

My research has indicated that there is a link between post traumatic stress disorder, repressed memories and a depressed cellular immunity. Cellular immunity is the part of the white cells that particularly fight viruses and cancer cells. It includes NK cells, B cells and T cells.

It is worthwhile here to describe the experiments of Dr Robert Ader, of the Rochester School of Medicine which formulate the basis for the effect of the brain on the immune system. He administered saccharin flavoured water to his laboratory rats and concurrently injected them with a drug that was known to suppress immunity as well as cause digestive disturbances. The rats rapidly began to avoid the flavoured water. However what was interesting was that a number of rats died when later they were offered the flavoured water without the drug being in it. Adler reasoned that this must have been a brain-triggered response. So using another group of rats, he set about conditioning them by giving the saccharin flavoured water and challenging them with a common antigen. He divided his rats into three groups.

- Group one received another injection of the drug ... result was depressed immunity as predicted.
- Group two was not treated further, that is they were not treated with the drug or given the flavoured water ... result was normal antibody response.
- Group three was given only the flavoured water without the drug ... result was a marked decrease in immune response. (The response to the challenge was significantly less than normal.)

Using some mechanism, the rats had learned to react to the flavoured water, giving the same response that they had to the immune-suppressing drug.

The conclusion is a most important one with many implications. Adler concluded that if learning could alter antibody response in this manner then a clear, direct link could be made between the brain and the immune system.

I would encourage you to think of this in the light of your learned behaviours and responses to life. For instance, enduring depression negatively affects the immune function. Something of great importance as far as the dietary component of the chemotherapy patient is concerned, is the importance of the type of food and liquid that you eat during the course of your chemotherapy treatment. Many patients are paying particular attention to juicing and special diets. I have had many patients who have reported that they drank quantities of carrot juice during their chemotherapy and after treatment could not even bear the smell of carrot juice. Sensitivities often develop after treatments with foods that were eaten during treatment phases. Since reading Adler's research and then having perused the many studies done over the following years I made a standard recommendation to my patients.

My recommendation was that those undergoing heavy drug treatment or chemotherapy should keep their diet simple especially during chemotherapy days or treatment weeks. This is to minimise the association of the brain-immune response between what is ingested and the chemistry of the drugs. I have also experienced this with some clients who become sensitive to environments, odours and other associated stimuli to an event or events. For instance they cannot go back to a chemotherapy ward without feeling ill. Some people are even sensitive to the colours of the room. This is a common response to associated trauma (PTSD) and is very individual. I had this response for some time after visiting the hospital unit where I had my first major bowel removal and ileostomy.

I mention this as a part of emotional healing; many patients have experienced these reactions in some form without realising the nature of the cause. They have become quite distressed by this, but when they understand the cause, their anxiety is relieved and they feel empowered to do something about it. Our food and environment, even the company we keep, can cause us stress and it is worth paying attention to what could be possible *stressors* in your environment and rectifying the situation.

Foods and Stress

The subject of food and the topic of food sensitivities in general needs to be discussed. Some foods can have a negative impact on our emotional states. It is possible that you may have become sensitive to certain foods during your treatments. It is also possible that you have had foods in your diet for some time that chemically do not agree with your metabolism. This can be a constant stress on your immune system and, in terms of health and wellbeing, can have a significant impact. I not only mean the foods that are preserved with chemical colourants or additives, but include natural foods such as milk, wheat, vegetables etc. Should you suspect any foods in your diet, you can test by simply eliminating the suspected food for one week to ten days and then re-introduce it into your diet later. Notice the response. Some of these sensitivities can be single substances while other people can have more complex combinations going on. Symptoms of these sensitivities can be constant fatigue (unrelieved by sleep), headaches, muscle or joint pains, and muscle weakness, to name but a few. Food sensitivities can take some sorting out; but the result is well worth the perseverance if you are one of this group of people. If you feel you cannot self manage; do consult a health therapist to help guide you through it.

Examining Attitudes to Stress

We need to develop a new attitude towards our understanding of stress and its role in our lives. Basically it comes back to a choice of how we deal with the key stressful issues. Dealt with on an "as you go along" basis we can learn to "roll with the punches" and develop resilience by paying attention to how we consciously deal with each situation. When these stressful episodes build up there is a cumulative effect and the result is that much self-care and healing is required. In terms of prevention, knowledge of the anatomy of stress is very helpful. With this knowledge we are empowered to make healthy choices and conscious choices about how we manage stress. We cannot eradicate stress from our lives but we can change our response to it. We can learn to view stressful situations as *manageable challenges, learning opportunities or take the view of accepting the situation for what it is*. Like fire, stress can be a good servant, but a bad master!

Of course our logical mind can make a decision easily on this matter, however, when stress becomes a part of our day-to-day existence and we react to it, we become emotionally hooked. Adrenaline is quite addictive and the effects of enduring stress, emotional joy or discord are recorded in the body. As neuroscientist Antonio Demasio wrote in his recent book: "*Emotions are played out in the theatre of the body!*"

The Survival Response

The *flight* or *fight* response, originally a mechanism of life preservation, is an instinctual response that heightens our senses allowing for rapid movement and, if necessary, incredible feats of strength on the spur of the moment. For instance, this innate response will cause you to move rapidly out of the way of an oncoming bus without thinking. The flight or fight response is activated by *fear* and has a profound biochemical effect in the body, causing symptoms of pounding heartbeat, sweaty palms, shallow and rapid breathing, elevated blood pressure and various hormonal responses. It is an adrenal response and, along with it, immune inhibiting hormones such as cortisol and adrenaline, flood into our bloodstream.

As humans have evolved, our stressors have changed substantially. We have evolved from times where our experience of stress was, for example, being chased by a sabre-tooth tiger that was trying to make a meal of us. Now we have new and different stressors as a part of modern living! With this lifestyle come all kinds of "mod cons" which, in theory, should be making our lives simpler. Instead the sabre-tooth tiger is replaced by the debts we owe, unwelcome responsibilities and dysfunctional marriages. Our battles are fought on the freeways at the end of a stressful day or in the home.

The opposite of the flight or fight response is what has become known as *the relaxation response*. This is best described as a state of naturally letting go, where balance, equilibrium, homeostasis and harmony are restored. It is experienced as the deep outward sigh or breath, the release after the adrenaline rush of the flight or fight response. It is the effect of letting go, which you will experience in the deep and profound state of relaxation or meditation.

For effective stress management, adopting the use of circuit breakers (mini relaxation response exercises), are helpful to practise throughout the day and will increase your wellbeing and life quality.

Most of us unconsciously react to stress in our lives not realising that the effects of stress records in our bodies just like we record a voice on to an audio tape. Our history dictates much of our day-to-day experience. Our past provides a platform, a background against which we habitually live our lives with our past dictating what we do. Concurrently, we tend to project our life into the future, hoping for a better life, a better deal, and a better hand of cards to be dealt. Finally there is the part of us, usually a very small part that is living right now, here in the moment. Bringing our past forward and our projected future back, can result in us experiencing living in the moment, in present time.

Fear: A Potent Stressor

June, a patient in a recent group, told us how impressed she had been with the power of fear. One of June's friends, who was diagnosed with a cancer that was not as serious as her own, died the morning after the diagnosis. The friend apparently had responded with incredible fear to her situation!

In India there is a parable told that highlights the potency of fear in our lives. It is called:

The Devil and the Pilgrim

One day the devil met a pilgrim walking along the roadside. The devil was rubbing his hands together, singing and very happy.

When the pilgrim asked him, "Devil, why are you so happy?" the devil replied: "Well, today I am going to kill ten thousand people."

"That's a tall order", said the pilgrim. "How could you possibly do that?"

"Oh, it is very easy if you know how", was the devil's reply. "All I have to do is kill one with cholera, and the rest will die of fear!"

Fear of illness and death are deeply woven into the fabric of our society. Fear can provide the extra fuel on which illness can flourish once it is diagnosed. Our response to fear can work either of two ways. It can motivate us to try or it can encourage us to switch off our life force. As we have seen from the flight or fight response, fear can change body chemistry significantly, sending out the danger alarm in a way that can give a message of being out of control. Eventually this can lead to an impaired response from our immune system to foreign invaders and cancer cells.

You may find it helpful to consider how you are responding to fear in your life. Recognise if this is an area that you need help with. For women dealing with breast cancer, fear can be a paralysing emotion, so much so that *the fear can become the disease.* Meditation and counselling can help with diminishing fear in your life. The "observer" can bring fears to your attention and help find solutions. One of the most helpful of the self-help tools, without doubt, is the development of a personal life philosophy, one in which you find life meaning. Finding life meaning dispels personal fear.

The Positive Side of Fear

The role of fear as a motivating influence is usually the first stage of the healing process. Fear can encourage you to galvanise your resources by moving you into survival mode, enabling you to consciously decide what to do about your diagnosis. Illness can provide an opportunity to change aspects of your life that you have put in the "too hard file". So many women have spoken to me of this, and of how their diagnosis came as a relief after a period of time where fear, dread and hopelessness had ruled their lives. Diagnosis for these women actually relieved their fear and gave them something concrete to focus on. For others the diagnosis may accentuate the many pre-diagnosis issues and culminate with fear induced by diagnosis

The story of Jan's courageous inner struggle to find healing may help you to understand these concepts on a practical level.

Jan's Story

"I had a mastectomy after a diagnosis of carcinoma of the breast. Five weeks later I returned to my work as a family therapist, working with children and families in violent and sexually abusive situations. This was a week after my husband had an emergency appendectomy. One month later he had a breakdown and would not return to full time work for six months. We were struggling in our twenty-two year old marriage. So I took up full time work and the following year took steps to start my Masters. I kept wondering if I had made enough changes to prevent getting secondaries, but I had made myself too busy to think too much about it.

Two years later a 4 cm × 8 cm (1.5 in × 3 in) mass was discovered in the right lobe of my liver and 2 cm (1 in) ones were scattered throughout the left lobe. I felt utterly devastated and full of self-blame for not making the necessary changes, full of guilt for the children's sakes and very angry. The doctors basically wrote me off, saying there was a very small chance that Tamoxifen would help, but I reluctantly decided to go on it. I attended a self-help residential programme and learned a lot. There were so many factors, including my perfectionist nature, living my life according to others' expectations, pleasing behaviours and feeling highly responsible that it was up to me to make people feel better and so on.

It felt like months of misery combined with a sense of panic and I was concerned that I did not have the positive attitude I needed to heal myself. But, I was also aware for the first time, that I was allowing myself to *feel* negative emotions instead of burying and denying them as I had always done, *out of fear as well as not wanting to show emotion in case others might judge me.*

Another year later, I decided to begin to face the prospect of death, moving past denial (oh it is so painful to face one's negativities) as a result of my terrible prognosis — 30% live two years, 5% live 10 years. Sogyal Rimpoche's book *The Tibetan Book of Living and Dying* helped me through this stage and I have no fear of death now.

A little time after I repeated the self-help programme and I began seeing a psychologist. He has been a wonderful support for me. I realised then that I could not return to part-time work and study as I had planned to. Whilst I felt well, I still needed to learn how to break the busy pattern of my life and be still and quiet. This was very traumatic as I faced my deep attachment to my identity as a therapist/senior team member/public servant. If I wasn't those things, who was I?

Investigations later that year showed that there were no tumours left in my liver! I was elated and had a party to thank all my friends and my poor parents, who had been so distressed, for all their prayers and support; so many of their friends and relatives had prayed for my recovery.

So, I gave it my all — meditating for 3 hours per day, looking after my nutrition and having 5 or 6 juices per day, vitamin supplements, exercise, etc. I had some very tough years as my daughter struggled with the separation and her fears about me dying, particularly during her final year at school. I see now how much I tried to protect them and not let them know how distressed I was feeling so much of the time, and how guilty I felt for getting sick.

I would do it differently now. Kids shouldn't be protected. They "know" anyway. It was a tough year too as I adjusted to living alone after twenty four years, being a single parent, having no money, selling the family house and being like my former clients on a disability pension. I discovered I had no real sense of who I was after all the years of living according to others' expectations. In my healing I began to accept that obstacles are a part of life and they are a major opportunity for growth and transformation."

Accentuate the Positive

When cancer is the illness it becomes so easy to concentrate exclusively on its presence. So much so that patients can forget to appreciate how much of them is still functional. Just think about it. One small lump of say, two centimetres (one inch) can paralyse a person just by its presence and the associated fear that it generates. They forget just how much of them is still well. This is not to take away the seriousness of a diagnosis or to be in denial but rather just to put it into perspective.

During a group session recently, there was a woman whose entire lower abdominal organs had been removed. However, despite an incredible surgical history, she looked fantastic. There was still lots left of her that was well and functional. She told the group that she had every intention of enjoying what was left! Considering what she had been through it would have been quite understandable for her to concentrate on her loss, but instead she chose to accent what she had left and enjoy life through new eyes: "A small price to pay!" she said.

Learned Optimism

Some people are naturally optimistic in life. There is a saying that optimists live longer. Pessimists are right but they don't live as long! Just because you are an optimist doesn't mean that you won't become ill or fall prey to one of life's catastrophic events. But it does mean that if you do, you are likely to handle it much better than the pessimist would. An optimist has developed a philosophical life view that gives meaning behind the events in their life. Natural optimism can be inherited or you may have had some positive conditioning as a child that has programmed you to "view the glass as being half full rather than half empty".

However, I believe that we can learn to be optimistic and be open to possibilities and one way to begin this process is to look at changing a habit. For beginners just one habit will do. For example, I knew a fellow who was always complaining about his shaving rash that would stay irritated for some hours after shaving. He really didn't like being "blotchy" but felt there was little he could do. He just had sensitive skin. I asked him whether or not he shaved before a shower or after a shower. The answer was that he had always shaved after his morning shower. I suggested that he try to shave before he showered and that it might make a difference and it did. Now this is a simple example but it highlights just how we get into the groove of doing something one way, a routine, habitual action without thinking about it. The key was that *he really wanted to do something* about his skin sensitivity and he was open to change and optimistic and keen to try. By making excuses about why you shouldn't change for example, I've always done it that way or by saying I would if I could but …, I know I should but … we stop ourselves from progressing and from changing habits that may no longer serve us. Learned optimism can be achieved by making small and do-able changes. Make changes in small increments. Just one small change each day adds up to quite a lot by the end of a week!

Immunity: Threat or Challenge — Our Choice

Researcher Steven Greer developed a useful parameter with his study on coping styles which looked at the various coping styles of women with breast cancer. Although it is a generalised approach, I have found it useful in terms of how to reach different types of women with the same information. However some therapists have used the information to stereotype who they might help and who they might not bother to help. I believe strongly that all women diagnosed with cancer deserve to at least see the options, whether they are considered hopeless and helpless or whether or not we know that we can muster a "fighting spirit". Most people do not like to be labelled, least of all cancer patients. The following story highlights my point.

Janice

Janice had developed a severe type of breast cancer that was quite advanced before she was diagnosed. The tumour had spread, showing extensive lymph node involvement. She had been quite depressed and appeared to be in the helpless, hopeless category when she came for her first appointment. However after a few sessions the "black cloud" lifted and she began to be open to possibilities. As a consequence she had joined a support group as a part of her hospital's oncology services. The leaders were nurses, with good intentions but no experience of conducting this type of group. Unknown to Janice, they graded the people who attended the groups in terms of their cancer type and severity. At the first session Janice sat in a waiting room with many other patients wondering why she had not gone in with the first group of women. She knew many of the group and they had already established a bond from their similar experiences in the oncology ward where she had her chemotherapy. The nurse came in and out calling people by name and directing them into different areas. So eventually Janice asked why she could not go with the first group. The nurse looked at her with a patronising gaze. She quickly checked the patient list and avoiding eye contact said: "I'm sorry Mrs H. but that group is only for the grade one tumours. You have a grade three tumour. You're a part of the smaller group over there, the palliative care group. I'm so sorry." Her voiced trailed off into the distance. Janice was devastated. She had very negative connotations about the word palliative as her mother had died of breast cancer whilst in palliative care. This happened at a vulnerable time when she was shifting from hopeless to hopeful. This story highlights the need for all medical and paramedical staff to be aware of the use of effective therapeutic language with cancer patients. The manner in which information is delivered can severely stress an already stressed patient. Much of this is, of course, not conscious; but cancer patients become very sensitive to information and body language concerning their condition and prognosis.

Women with breast cancer who respond to their illness as a life challenge, who realise that their diagnosis faces them with their own mortality, will often be the women who begin actively to search for solutions outside of what orthodox medicine has to offer. These women find something to live for, quickly passing through the hopeless and helpless phase which may have been evident prior to diagnosis. Their cancer has given them an opportunity for profound change. Their immune systems respond accordingly for, as you will recall, the brain "talks" to the immune system and vice versa. This can be quite an active time and for some is necessary, using fear as the prime motivator for change. It can be a good short-term strategy for motivation; but is a poor long-term strategy due to the stress cycle that proactive patients tend towards. They can easily become stressed by trying too hard to de-stress. Women diagnosed with breast cancer, often motivated by the flight or fight response, are frequently inspired by the thought that *they do not want to die.*

Women who remain hopeless and helpless with their spirit dulled, their stress or grief unresolved and their feelings constantly denied, can have a harder path to recovery. With motivation lacking, negative messages about their condition and maybe inadequate support systems or isolation, their internal messages become an obstacle to healing. They may accept the possibility of death more easily and see it as a solution with total acceptance. As much as we need to allow people to have the opportunity to seize the options that are available, we also need to allow people the power of choice not to heal or recover. We never know the destiny of another. In a world of therapies that promote the "fix it" mentality, I have learned that not everything that is broken needs "fixing". All diseases are curable, all people are not. Those that choose to heal and succeed tend, to quote Hemingway, *"to grow strong at the broken places"*.

Chapter Ten

The Art of De-Stressing

My first involvement with the practice of meditation and relaxation was when my partner was diagnosed with secondary bone cancer. Meditation practice was a part of our healing programme and although it wasn't directly responsible for his remission, it was an important part of our daily healing programme. Although not curative per se, meditation incorporated with various other methods for self-discovery, was a very meaningful tool. One of the additions that made it even more effective was the combined use of touch with meditation. Sometimes a meditation session would involve us sitting next to each other, other times I would give him a body massage and magnetic healing as he meditated. Often he would lie upon the bed for his meditation, not usually recommended because of the association of the bed with sleeping. However it was due to his high degree of pain, that the prone position was helpful. Don't become too fixed upon the "must dos" and "must not dos" concerning meditation. It's important to remain flexible and once you know the basics, you can tailor these methods and practices to your individual needs. There is certainly ample scientific evidence that the practice of relaxation and meditation can alter brain and body chemistry and improve the quality of your life. As one client said many years ago: "I don't care anymore whether meditation treats cancer; all I know is that it just makes your life better!"

Defining Meditation

Meditation is a non-doing, non-striving activity that helps us to be focused in the experience of "now" — this present moment, this present time. Meditation is not designed to "space you out" and separate you from your awareness and consciousness as is believed by many. Rather meditation is designed to "space you in" in to yourself.

Meditation can mean many things to many different people. In attempting to define what the practice of meditation is, we need to look at the needs of the people using it. Commonly it is associated with spiritual pursuits in both Eastern and Western religious practices. During the last thirty years, meditation seems to have secured a place in Western society due to the influx of many teachers from India and Tibet, in particular. Although this has been a good introduction, unfortunately it has also served to create a cloud of mystique around meditation. Many people feel that it is not a practice that could be easily incorporated into the hustle and bustle of their busy lives. Also, these various associations or alignments with religions, spiritual groups or cults have often been an issue for people who just want to use meditation for health purposes. I have often had feedback from patients who feel changed by learning to really let go physically using these deep relaxation methods. This then followed on to helping them develop a spiritual dimension to their lives. As a patient once said "There's nothing like a diagnosis of a life-threatening illness to get you questioning the meaning of life and the nature of God!"

Should you wish to pursue a more spiritual form of meditation, just as with applying imagery, it is my suggestion that it is valuable first to learn the techniques for deep relaxation. Then, when you are proficient at being able to relax your body, apply whatever spiritual practice or imagery you choose to, while you are in the state of deep relaxation. Once you have learned a method of meditation that works for you, you can apply it in your everyday life. The great thing about this as a self-help technique is that it always accessible, you can take it with you anywhere, it has no harmful side effects, and it is free!

Overview

For our purposes we will concentrate on one type of meditation practice — a practice of restoring health, accelerating healing and stimulating immunity.

So maybe you are a beginner with an interest in learning the techniques of meditation and relaxation. Perhaps you have tried to meditate and feel frustrated by going to sleep or you are becoming frustrated by trying too hard to stop thoughts and still the mind. There are many pitfalls for the novice meditator. When someone explains meditation for the first time, logically it sounds do-able, easy in theory; but putting the theory into practise is where so many become frustrated and give up. If you are keen to explore meditation as an addition to your healing programme it is helpful to know *what* you are doing and *how* to do it! In particular the urgency that a diagnosis of cancer brings can be a pressure to learn quickly and that then becomes an obstacle to your progress. The pressure of getting it right, for many, can become just another stress to do another therapy to add to the laundry list of stresses.

Deep relaxation and meditation are not therapies per se, but rather they are a way of life! To be effective they need to filter through into your life. If you perceive them as a treatment, you tend to start looking for results and thus start the cycle of trying to achieve the perfect practice. If you are looking for a teacher, try to find someone with experience in working with people with cancer and who understands the importance of working with the stress stored in the body. This is relevant for those who are not ill but who want to learn how to better handle stress and their response to it. A daily practise of some form of deep relaxation or meditation is the best preventive medicine that you can do. As an addition or if you have trouble sitting still, Yoga, Qigong and Tai Chi are helpful practices as moving meditations and are highly recommended.

First Things First

Before we move into discussing some practical exercises, let us first explore the importance of using a body-focused method of meditation. Meditation is elusive, hard to describe. The best description of the practice I have heard is that it is like trying to describe the taste of a banana to someone when they have never tasted a banana before! I meditated (or thought I was), for many years, enduring much frustration until I realised that meditation for health and healing is different from the classic spiritual approaches. I was sailing around the various spiritual practices like a ship without a rudder.

However many years ago, when I was teaching meditation I had a personal "aha" of enormous magnitude that changed both my personal practice and the way I taught meditation to others from that day onwards! Imagine a room with twenty meditating people, all seated and *trying hard to meditate*. This group has been together for six weeks and had experienced three different group leaders during that time. As I walked around the room, I couldn't help but observe the obvious tension in their bodies. Some of them gripped on to the arms of the chairs with white knuckles evident; others sat with clenched jaws, and eyes that were either so tightly closed that the skin wrinkled up around them or that the skin of their forehead became etched into a frown. I remember walking quietly around the circle for some time observing what was happening to their bodies as they sat. When the session concluded, I asked each person what his or her experience had been. Almost all said that they had never felt so relaxed! They *were* being truthful because they **thought** they were relaxed! However it was obvious to my eye that their bodies were having a different experience to their minds and were reflecting their true state of *tension*. The few people in the group who said that they had problems relaxing actually *were*

116

listening to and connecting with their body and what they were hearing was their body's *truth*. Here is the "aha!" Just because you ask your body to relax does not necessarily mean that it will obey. Often in the busy-ness of our daily lives we become unaware of how our body is responding to the stresses and strains. We don't notice or we ignore the stress building up in our body until something goes wrong. Unless it hurts or breaks down we tend to ignore it. It is as if the body tags along with the head as if the body was just going along for the ride! We try in modern life to rule our bodies with our heads! Hence when we consciously try to relax our body the head (mind) has another experience altogether! This is *not* mind-body medicine as there is no connection, no effective communication, between the two. So, if you are not connecting, not *present*, that is, not connecting to your body, where are you?

Well, you are likely to be in the place where the mind drifts away, detaches to a similar place to the place of daydreams. If you have endured trauma and have PTSD this separation can become even more marked as you dissociate from the experience of the being in your body. This is important to understand if you are using these techniques for healing and recovery. Learning, or being comfortable with, the dissociation or the separation of mind from body, is helpful in certain circumstances only. One is with managing severe pain or unpleasant painful procedures and the other is that practising separation can help us to die well, which after all is the ultimate separation! A peaceful death with ease and dignity has been experienced by many that have chosen meditation as their way of life.

This also relates to those who have anorexia, bulimia and even to drug addicts. There is a habitual drive that leads to an addiction to experiencing the feeling of being out of their body. For many reasons people can habitually desire to be "out there" that is, *removed* from their body rather than "in there" that is, *connected and present* to their body. The same applies to the practises of imagery or visualisation; the more present you are, the more effectively the image will help. Also someone who is very ill with cancer and who is not eating will, through lack of food, experience this separating out of the consciousness. This work has far reaching implications for the health of us all.

How Can We Become More Aware?

Deep relaxation teaches us to be more aware, to notice the effects of stress in the body as they happen, so that we can then diffuse it before we store it as tension in our shoulders, jaws, forehead or in whatever part of the body we store our stresses. This, of course, is different for different people. These methods need to flow into your daily life. For instance, if you have a session at home and leave the house not taking the benefits with you, as one of my mentors Sogyal Rimpoche says: *"It is like leaving your elephant at home and looking for its footprints in the forest!"*

Often those new to meditation can experience a sense of frustration at not being able to still the mind immediately. Because we are used to achieving in life, the process of meditation proves not to be easy in the beginning, as it does not follow our expected "work equals result" mentality. However, a method of deep relaxation that begins its work in the body first, can have effects that are quickly noticed. In particular, often women will notice immediate help with relief from fatigue and insomnia. The practice of deep relaxation helps to establish healthy boundaries and build resilience. The day-to-day stresses that previously would have affected you now deflect "like water off a duck's back". Previously you may have absorbed the stresses of others that led to you feeling fatigued. Methods that increase your awareness as well as maintaining a practice of deep relaxation is the beginning of how we change the pattern of withholding, to the pattern of letting go. You first need to be aware, and then the process of letting go of withheld stress, using simple methods, follows on. My advice is to develop and use different kinds of awareness exercises or find practitioners in the many fields of complementary therapies who deal with increasing body awareness (for example the Feldenkrais Technique). The stumbling block for most people who try to learn meditation for health purposes, is that they have often lost a good deal of body awareness and their boundaries are already compromised. Therefore, before beginning the mind practice it is very helpful to make contact and connect with the body.

So, our method of meditation will be a practice that concentrates on the profound relaxation of the body and which, over a period of time, will lead to de-stressing. Don't be too preoccupied with stopping thoughts, slowing down or stilling the mind. It will all naturally follow. Anyway I was told once by a Tibetan lama that thoughts were not of concern. He said that even the Dalai Lama has thoughts when he meditates!

Our tool to accomplish this will be the progressive muscle relaxation exercise (PMR). This method has long been a tool taught and used by Yoga practitioners. I believe it works best however when practised regularly. I have meditated for nearly thirty years now and every day, I still begin my session with the PMR by contracting and relaxing muscles throughout my entire body. I have learned to practise the technique very quickly now so that I can use it even when out shopping or quickly during the course of a stressful day. Our aim will be to concentrate thoroughly on our body, becoming more present by focusing our conscious awareness sequentially throughout each large muscle group. The experience of a profound level of relaxation very quickly, leads to a direct feeling of wellbeing.

How to Begin a Practice of Deep Relaxation and Meditation

Essentially the desire to meditate needs to come from you. It requires your motivation and a belief that it will do you some good. If your feeling is one of being "stuck", powerless or helpless, begin very simply by just doing a few simple exercises every day so that you build up confidence and you start to feel some effect. Simple mindfulness exercises are helpful, as are short bursts of relaxation throughout the day. Don't set yourself goals that you cannot achieve otherwise you will set yourself up to fail!

To begin the practices of meditation, and to maintain your practice so that you feel its benefits, you will probably require *effort*, *perseverance* and *determination*. These may not be qualities that you would usually associate with the actual practice of the gentle art of meditation, however they are essential as initiators to the process. Establish a routine morning and evening and in the middle of the day if necessary and adhere to it for the first month.

Ideally choose a time of day when it will be possible to have some time to yourself. Choose a place where distractions such as telephones, including mobile phones, are out of range. Be creative and use an answer-phone if necessary to get some quiet time. If at home and you are concerned about being disturbed, write a note on your door telling people to return another time and don't feel guilty for doing it! Many people, when they first begin meditation find that using a Walkman with comfortable earphones can help them to screen out background noise. I suggest that you use guided relaxation/meditation tapes or CDs during the learning phase. This helps you to focus and keep your attention. Later on you can graduate to using some relaxing classical music. The type of music is important, as you need help to be present, aware and grounded. New age music can be pleasant to listen to; but sometimes is not helpful in keeping you grounded.

Once your meditation is established, however, you will no doubt find that noises come and go and do not bother you at all. Tapes can still be used occasionally, especially at times of heightened stress in your life when your concentration may be a little lacking. Of course, these stressful times are the times when your meditation needs to be a priority — the times when you need to practise the most. So beware that you do not sabotage your practice by letting it slip by at the time when you need it most.

What to Expect

Establishing a time of day when you can practice, will give rhythm and consistency to your meditation. While you are learning, it is best not to meditate at times close to appointments, school runs, etc, as when you are new to the practice, you may be concerned about going to sleep and become anxious about being on time. Meditation is an "in-the-moment", present-time experience, which you will quickly learn to enjoy. If you are normally a very active type of person, beginning with some exercise may be useful. You may find that a brisk walk around the block, in a park or maybe on a nearby beach will help you to meditate more effectively This will enable your muscles to let go, and relax more easily. "Walking out" some of the tension from your body, just prior to your meditation session, is the solution for active people whose muscles can tend to twitch and jump about during a relaxation period.

As you take up your position to commence your meditation, remind yourself of its purpose. You might make a simple affirmation like, "This is my time to relax, let go and allow healing to flow". Having done that, having set the attitude or atmosphere in which the meditation will take place, abandon any sense of striving or trying. This process is an effortless one. Just be.

To help with this process, find yourself a chair with a back and preferably arms, a chair that is not so comfortable that you nod off to sleep instead of meditating. Meditation is quite a conscious process carried out with awareness, whereas sleep is a process of being unconscious, unaware. It is frequently asked if one can tell whether you have been asleep or

121

meditating? You will definitely know the difference between sleep and meditative practice when you finish your session. Sleep will cause you to feel tired and heavy when you have finished your session whereas the meditation will give you a different quality of feeling. It is described as a feeling of muscles being heavy, combined with a heightened state of awareness. Many notice the outline of their body while in the relaxed state. This is when meditation practice can strengthen and reinforce your boundaries and heighten your consciousness. You will feel enlivened, with a sense that time has passed by quite quickly.

However, do not be too surprised if you do go to sleep at the first few attempts at meditation. As fatigue, stress and busy-ness have been your reality, you may find that your body so welcomes the opportunity to consciously relax, that you will go into a deep and restful sleep. Go with the flow. For a week or so, you may need the rest and if concerned about it, set an alarm clock (with a gentle alarm) to conclude your session. However do not confuse this sleep with meditation.

If you have a need, due to your physical state, to practise your meditation lying down on the floor or on a bed, by all means do so. Do be aware that the possibility of going to sleep is real. The technique of progressive muscle relaxation can be very helpful in dealing with pain and is also a good way of "relaxing down" the body before bed. Be aware however, that the benefits of meditation and sleep are quite different. Practising your meditation in the morning, rather than at the end of a busy day can be helpful. Meditation in the morning is like "charging your inner batteries" before the day begins. Meditation when you are tired is more like catching up. It becomes more like maintenance work which I call "damage control" meditation.

Time Management

Self-care, which includes making time for self, needs to be addressed. Women will often do everything for everyone else first and then, if there is time they will do something for themselves. As a tendency, women will put their own needs on the backburner and eat the burnt toast! So my suggestion is that you make a commitment to take time out, tell your family and friends that you are now taking time for yourself. Plan a time of say two hours daily to begin with. That is your time to focus on getting well. This does not include the time you spend going out to doctors and therapists.

It has been my experience with meditation practice that results can vary depending on the amount of time that you dedicate to it. The ranges seem to vary from fifteen to twenty minutes per day for healthy people, and up to three half-hour sessions per day for those dealing with life-threatening illness. Again, all people being individual means that the length of time required to effect the desired benefit will vary. Usually though, once you have "touched" the experience of such a profound state of rest, you are keen to keep going because it makes you feel so good.

My general recommendation for women with breast cancer is three half-hour sessions of meditation daily as a starting point, increasing the length of time as you feel the need and the benefit. This can also depend on the severity of the illness as well as the impact of medical treatments on your general health. I recommend that relaxation/meditation be practised throughout all your treatments and tests. It is well recognised that relaxation/meditation, especially when combined with imagery, can lead to the lessening of side effects quite dramatically.

Experiencing the Experience: Some Simple Exercises

The following exercises will provide you with an experience of the quality of feeling that you can expect from a practice of meditation. For the purpose of the exercise I will focus on three key areas where stress is recorded and held: the breath, the shoulders and the jaw. Attention to these three areas can make an enormous difference to the outcome of your session.

These exercises can be practised either sitting in a chair or lying down on the floor.

In the Chair: If you choose to sit, your position is important. Do not sit in a chair that makes you slump. If you can imagine the enormous statues of Rameses at the temple of Abu Simbel, that is the ideal position; your back against the back of the chair, feet flat upon the floor, eyes looking straight ahead.

On the Floor: If you choose to lie down a thin mat or duvet on the floor makes for sufficient cushioning. Use only a small pillow to support your neck and head. Do draw your knees up with feet flat upon the ground, knees pointing to the ceiling. This takes pressure off your lower back when lying down on the floor.

Try these exercises by first reading and doing them from the book and then learn them. They are excellent to practise before you begin your relaxation or meditation practice.

The Breath

Experiment one

Follow these steps:

1. With your eyes open, slowly take a deep breath, hold it for a moment then gently sigh out your breath. Notice what that feels like.
2. Now allow your eyes to gently close and repeat the above. Notice any difference
3. This time, with eyes open, take in a long, slow, deep breath, hold it for a moment and then deeply sigh out your breath with the sound of ahhhhhh. To make this sound requires you to release muscle tension. The sound seems to well up from the area of your navel. Your jaw should be relaxed and your lips apart. What do you

notice? Repeat this a couple of times and when you are familiar with that, move on to the next step.

4. Allow your eyes to gently close and repeat the long slow breath and sound. Ensure that when you release your breath, you allow it to leave your lungs imagining them as if they were a large balloon and all the air was being slowly pushed out.

5. With your eyes closed, experiment by alternating between the two different styles of breath and notice how your body feels. The long slow ahhhhhh is the *relaxation response*.

You may have noticed that during this short exercise, once you knew the technique, you became focused on the breath and your thought processes did not get in the way.

The Shoulders

Experiment two

If you are sitting for this exercise, remember to sit straight in your chair.

1. Draw or bunch your shoulders inwards and upwards towards your ears and hold them in that position until the count of five. Then, just let them drop back to their original position.
   Notice how this feels.

2. Now *very slowly* draw or bunch your shoulders inwards and upwards. Take at least four times as long as last time. Hold them to the count of five and then slowly allow them to descend. When they are almost back to their natural position allow your shoulders to move outwards a little so that your arms are slightly away from your body. Allow your shoulders to drop or sink under their own weight.
   Notice how this feels.

3. Repeat the two steps above, alternating from step one to step two.
   Notice the difference.

4. Now co-ordinate your long deep breath of experiment one (the relaxation response) with step two. Be very mindful and slow and remember that when you begin to allow your shoulders to sink downwards to let your deep breath go naturally making the ahhhhhh sound as the shoulders descend. Repeat this a few times.
   What do you notice?
5. Finally once you know step four, practise with your eyes closed and once again notice the difference.

The Jaw

Experiment three

A great deal of tension can be stored in and around your jaw.

1. Allow your mouth and jaw to slide from side to side. Then open and close your mouth as if you were having a large yawn. Do this for a few moments, experiencing and noticing what the quality of your jaw is. Is it tight, easy, tense, rigid, sore etc?
2. Then gently close your eyes and very slowly slide your mouth and jaw as before. Slowly open and close as before. Allow your jaw to be still. Take a long deep breath in and when you deeply sigh out your breath making the sound of ahhhhhh, ensure that your jaw is easeful and that your lips are gently parted. Notice the area around the joint of your jaw. How does it feel to you? Is there a difference?

You may need to remind yourself of these simple exercises several times throughout your day. Practise them before a meditation session or use them during the day to disperse any stress build up. They act as a habit changer, a circuit breaker to break the stress cycle.

Mindfulness

Many accidents happen because "our mind is somewhere else". This is the place we go to if we live our lives in the future rather than in the present moment. For instance, if you are cutting a tomato on the kitchen bench, but your mind is on collecting children from school or auntie visiting tomorrow you are more likely to cut your finger. This is an example of not being mindful; that is, not being present, not living in the moment. The practices of deep relaxation/meditation and awareness help to bring you more into the moment. It does take concentration and focus; but the more present you are, the more empowered, energetic and grounded you will be. Remember that cross-cultural wisdom tells us: "In order to heal you need to be present". The practice of mindfulness can help tremendously with applying your deep relaxation/ meditation in your daily life. Begin simply. Each day choose one of your usual routine activities. It might be cleaning your teeth or preparing and drinking your morning cup of tea. The method is to stop for a moment and think about what you are going to do. Think of the slowness and grace of a Thai dancer or of someone practising their Tai Chi. Then, proceed, bringing awareness, concentration and focus to your chosen activity. Each day or week you can choose a different activity or just practice the one activity. Very soon you will notice that your ability to be in the moment increases and a certain quality is added to your life. Appropriately, the Buddhist definition of meditation is "to bring the mind home".

What to Expect from the Practice of Meditation

As a result of your practise you will be gently changing the messages that have been going from the mind to the body. The message to the muscles now will be one of effortless ease. With this will come a feeling of peace and wellbeing.

Once we begin to establish this new pattern of response to stress, it is time to take it from the meditation room at home and "road-test" how it works for you out in the world. The benefits that you have established at home will stand you in good stead, but it is in your daily life that the meditation will go to work for you during and after your recovery.

If you choose to, you can go back to doing all the things you did before the diagnosis. The difference now will be that you will go back with a different attitude, and new ways of responding to the stresses in your life. And that is what will help you to enjoy good health and wellbeing. If your pattern has been one of withholding you can now operate with a new habit, a habit of letting go!

Chapter Eleven

Withheld Emotions

Deal with Them as They Arise

Step one

When withheld emotions arise within you, it can be helpful to immediately identify what the emotion is. If you have been practising meditation, you are likely to be able to find the areas in your body that are affected by stress. Your body is like an emotional resonator that can give you the necessary feedback and indicate when your emotional state is in overload and inducing a physical response. Most people can relate to the feeling of "butterflies" in the stomach when they are nervous, a draining feeling or some other noticeable shift somewhere in their body. It will be different for different people. The same principle operates for identifying areas of stress in the body.

Step two

Name the feeling or emotion. For instance, if resentment is the feeling, identify it by *name* and then ask yourself why you are experiencing it? (If you don't get an answer or don't know just leave it. Sometimes we don't always know why.) Ask yourself where are you feeling the emotion in your body? Then ask yourself if the result of this resentment is worth hanging on to? Who will it damage? Recognise that you have a choice in how to deal with it. Do you consciously choose to hang on to the resentment or to let it go? This technique can give you an insight into your reactions. Denial can also be a choice but not a recommended one. It may be that the feeling of resentment is totally justifiable. Many of these withheld emotions can be justified, however the *secret* of dealing with them is to experience the emotion in the moment and then not to hold on to it. Just consider that you will be the likely one to wear the damage, not the person being resented. Choose to let it go. It is a statement of empowerment that you have the ability to *choose* as to whether or not you hang on to the feeling or emotion. Therefore you are approaching the situation from a potent point of strength, named choice.

Step three

After your emotion is experienced and named, feel the emotion. Feel it in your body and feel it leaving your body. Use your breath, the big deep breath out with the sound of ahhhhhh just as you learned using the meditation technique.

Close your eyes, take a deep breath in and deeply sigh out the breath, feeling the emotion in your body dissolve and dissipate as the breath is exhaled. You can even imagine that the resentment has a form or colour that you may feel helps you to let it go with the breath. Some people use prayer or affirmations at this time. With each out-breath consciously relax, allowing the breath to drop down into the body. Take time for yourself after this process. Maybe even take a bath or shower if necessary. Afterwards writing a journal about the experience is as helpful as closure. Don't do too much at once and always remember if you feel you need help or support with the process, consult a counsellor or psychotherapist.

But what if the resentment is old, or the people that caused the resentment are dead, and we still carry it with us? What do you do then?

Ritual: A Woman's Way of Healing

If you feel haunted by or are aware that an old grief or memory is somehow retarding your life, the symbolic power of ritual may be the answer. Ritual connects with a part of the brain known as the limbic system, using the language of symbols. Over the years I have helped many women to find creative rituals that help them to release and come to terms with loss.

Loss is a major wound whether it is loss of a body part, a loved one, a home, a mother country, a job, to name but a few. Loss has many facets.

A ritual requires:

- A conscious desire and intention to let go of the effects of the loss.
- A desire for closure.

You will need

- Appropriate symbols for the loss.
- Right timing for the ritual. Usually this is sensed by the person concerned. For instance you cannot tell someone when you think they should do their ritual.
- Plan and think the ritual through so it has a definite beginning and a definite closure.
- Choose the right environment. Some like to invite friends to witness the event, but privacy is okay too.

As an example I will share with you an event of showing the significance of ritual in my own life.

In 1997 I had a total prolapse of my uterus. This occurred three days after my husband had separated from me. During my marriage I had had five pregnancies and four children. I was a fiercely protective and vigilant mother whose femaleness was, and still is, a cherished quality. I felt extremely traumatised by the whole experience, knowing the losses that were ahead of me and grieving the loss of the years behind me. I was not ready to lose my uterus. It was all too much to manage at once, as everything had happened so quickly. I soon found myself, by necessity, having a hysterectomy.

I knew I had to devise some sort of ritual in order to keep my sanity; just as I had advised other women suffering loss to do. I asked the hospital theatre assistant if I could have my uterus in formalin. I think it was the first time a patient had ever asked for such a thing! But when I awoke from my anaesthetic, there it was beside my bed (covered over for the sake of visitors!). When home from hospital I reserved a safe spot for it in the house and gave some thought about what I might do with it. I had six difficult months of grieving. Without knowing at the time of the hysterectomy that I had sustained severe nerve damage, the uterus was there to remind me as a symbol of my reproductive years — a symbol of many things past and now behind me.

One day I just felt it was the right time. A friend had given me a beautiful flowering "Lady of the Night" magnolia which I decided to plant on top of my poor old, by now well pickled uterus. With just myself present I dug a large hole, placed the uterus in the earth and mindfully planted the tree. The whole process took about an hour. I was ready to let go of it. Like many women who undergo a hysterectomy my sexuality had felt challenged. As well, the nerve damage had left me severely numbed and with a paralysed rectum and bowel problems. However, the day I performed my ritual burial, in fact within an hour, an old friend called me to ask if I would like to go to a formal ball with a blind date. That night I met a really wonderful man who brought some friendship, joy and intellectual stimulation into my life. His company really helped me through the next few months as I regained my sense of self again. Despite my condition I can pinpoint that day as the day when I was ready to move on. When I became re-empowered to meet the enormous medical challenges and battles that, unknown to me at that time, lay before me. This is the power of conscious ritual. This is the soul medicine of women.

Forgiveness as a Solution — Letting Go

Of course it sounds logical to the rational mind that forgiveness is a great idea. It really makes sense to let go of issues which we know will ultimately harm us. So why is forgiveness such a difficult thing for us to achieve? One reason commonly discussed in our groups is that by forgiving someone we may validate what they have done to us, making us a victim of their future actions. Others may think that revenge is justified and essential, that there should be an eye for an eye and a tooth for a tooth!

It is a fact of human nature that revenge is sweeter than forgiveness. Think how many wars have been initiated by this one potent emotion. We are dealing here with a form of action that is inherent in our society, which is why it is so hard to deal with on a personal basis. Another difficulty people have with forgiveness is that the withheld emotions, like revenge and resentment, can give us a hold on people whom we love and whom we fear may abandon us. Resentment may allow us to hold on to a relationship, even if the quality of that relationship is poor — to say the least. In some cases too, it can be a case of better the devil you know than the one you do not!

It has been my experience that many women with breast cancer wrestle deeply with the issue of forgiveness. So many of these women who have been trying to cope, trying to be a perfect and loving wife, have had incredible issues concerning resentment and anger. Often these emotions have never been expressed but have been denied in order to survive. How long can they be held in the psyche before they are mirrored in the body? Feeling betrayed is often another big issue. I see many women with breast cancer after the breakdown of a significant relationship that has led to either divorce or separation. Issues of prolonged stress, suspicion, shock, betrayal, loss of self-esteem and resentment that are all withheld, can blaze a trail towards illness.

The more I talk about forgiveness with groups of cancer patients, the more aware I become of so many different opinions of what forgiveness really is. Forgiveness is based on being non-judgmental and a premise that we are all essentially the same at the core of our being. The practice of forgiveness is a freeing process from which we can grow to a point of compassion and understanding of why the other has wronged us in some way. True forgiveness can result in cutting the unpleasant ties that can bind us to others through the use of guilt, blame and shame and the resultant toxic relationship. Forgiveness involves us in setting boundaries in our life and defining what is acceptable for us. Forgiveness is ultimately an experience that will open up the pure loving energy of our heart. All this is very easy to say but very hard indeed in some cases to put into practice.

The Necessity of Forgiveness

In my experience, if an event or the results of an event are consciously dominating your life long after the incident is past, then forgiveness, compassion, understanding and love are the remedies required.

Seek expert counselling if you are unconscious of what the issues are that are causing you to be ill at ease. All people being different and individual, means that some may need guidance and support along the way. At first glance, all aspects of forgiveness sound good. The advantages appear to be loaded our way. So again, why is so difficult to offer true forgiveness and mean it? One of the biggest dilemmas for people who begin the practice of forgiveness is the realisation that when the forgiving is complete, the relationship with the person they have forgiven may change. With forgiveness comes a letting go. Once you have let go both parties then have the freedom to choose either total acceptance or the freedom to move on in life; often without carrying the excess baggage of guilt and blame with them.

If you have totally forgiven someone and they continue to repeat their mistakes again and again and they injure you, this is abuse. This can happen because you have in your original forgiveness set a precedent as to the type and amount of habitual behaviour that you are prepared to accept from this person. If you made up your mind to forgive on those occasions you can also choose where to draw the line in the sand. From there you are empowered by your choice. You may not know when or how but you do have conscious intention to choose your appropriate course of action. Forgiveness may result from the recognition that some of your relationships have not been life enhancing ones.

So, again, once you forgive someone you may have to let him or her go *and* you may have to let go of him or her. To then trust that they will choose to maintain the relationship free of the bonds of resentment, guilt or shame is fraught with danger — that is a trust which asks a lot of us! I think that this fear of lost relationship is why many people who think that they want to forgive, find it so hard in practice.

These are facts of life that do not seem to be acknowledged enough by many who write about forgiveness. Maybe working entirely with life-threatening illness has given me a realistic view of how difficult it really is for these women to practise forgiveness. I feel it is so much easier to forgive when you are well, but so often we do not get the impetus or the inclination until we have physical symptoms to deal with. I have known patients to survive for several years hanging on to their resentments and denying their need for forgiveness. However, these are the same people who, on their deathbed, have seen the need to attend to this "unfinished business", let it go and heal their souls before moving into death.

So, to me it seems it is very much a personal choice as to the time we begin to forgive. But do be aware, it seems that to not attend to forgiveness in your life is like beginning a journey on a road that has a large boulder on it blocking your way. The only way through is to shift it.

The practice of forgiveness is the way to the *heart* of the matter, the way to release your negative blocks to healing. It is an issue of personal choice, but one that goes beyond our mental processes. Where forgiveness is concerned, it is not what you mentally believe about it, but where and how you emotionally feel it, that makes the difference. Forgiveness will work better for you if you are on the journey of self-discovery and searching for life meaning. You can't just think that you have forgiven someone. Like the mind-body connection exercises described in this book, your head must connect and communicate to your body and then your body needs to respond if it has been understood. Forgiveness is like that. When you really have accomplished it, it is felt in every cell in your body. Authentic forgiveness is an unmistakable feeling. Forgiveness cannot be pretended to be happening.

When anger and resentment are held within us we become deaf to the language of our own heart and our flow of love is impeded to ourselves and others.

J. Krishnamurti said of love:

"Of all the qualifications, Love is the most important, for if it strong enough in a man (or woman), it forces him (or her) to acquire all the rest, and all the rest without it would never be sufficient."

Forgiveness will not eradicate the memories associated with events in your life that you would rather forget. Forgiveness is a conscious process. What it will do however is to help by removing the emotional "sting" that often accompanies a bad memory or experience. Like the removal of a bee-sting it will be painful for a while, but then as happens with the removal of the bee sting, the inflammation and response will settle and the healing will begin.

Guilt and Shame

These are two powerful conditions that can keep women, men and families in silence. Issues associated with these conditions can reach way back into our lives. They can often originate from conditionings associated with belief systems and behaviours from our past. Also they can both originate from your family history. Shame particularly, can be transferred down through your family; that is, you can be a product of a shame-bound family. You know if you have this type of shame because you cannot identify anything at all from this current life that could cause you to be shameful.

When we carry guilt with us, we often deny it and our behaviour is the only key to identifying its presence. It makes itself known by the constant, unhealthy choices that we make in our lives. This will mirror in our day-to-day life as low self-esteem. When this is the case we can easily be manipulated by others in our environment, which, of course, becomes a continuous life cycle. It is made more complex because guilt and shame, although unconsciously held within us, have the power to insidiously destroy us. Unhealthy guilt offers no promise of positive healing or transformation, but what it can do, is to lead us further into other destructive patterns of behaviour, including depression. Shame on the other hand can be at the root cause of addictive, abusive and compulsive behaviours.

It is my hope that the issues presented within the pages of this book can stimulate awareness of the importance of dealing with major life events in a positive way. It is quite a natural process when old emotions are woken up to have a sense of blame, guilt or some form of self-punishment. Remember to be gentle with yourself, concentrating on the fact that you did your best at the time. It is important not to punish yourself even more. It may be that it is yourself whom you will need to forgive first and foremost.

As children we may have carried the burden of guilt from our parents and voluntarily taken on the responsibility to heal the pain and to somehow try to make things right in the family. Children often tend to do this to hide the real pain in their family life. It is a major issue for the children of alcoholic parents to deal with. Often they had to put a lot of energy into trying to make it right at home, while at the same time, trying to hide their shame and guilt from the outside world.

Guilt can only be dealt with and healed when it becomes accessible to the conscious mind. This awareness to the presence of guilt and shame can be difficult to work with, initially due to the power of denial that accompanies it.

You may find that as a natural consequence of your healing journey, these issues may naturally arise as a result of your practice of meditation. Meditation can act like a filtering device for the more unreachable parts of our psyche. It can also be a good practice for clarifying issues. Like muddied water, if left for long enough the mud will eventually settle out and the water will clear. So too do our issues such as guilt and shame. But it does take commitment and intention to clear these old patterns. They can inhibit the flow of your life by keeping you hooked into the negative aspects of your family "trance". The "trance" is best described as the denial of *shadow* and the absence of memory concerning issues that previous generations did not address. We inherit these like ghosts from the past as a consequence of conditioning and genetics. The *shadow* is a term that is used for all that is not conscious. References on the subject of shame and guilt are listed in the back of this book.

Mothers, Daughters and Emotional Healing

A woman can carry deep wounds that result from a lack of nurturing in her life. There may be feelings of grief, abandonment and helplessness. As a result there can be guilt, blame and shame associated with these issues. Often she cannot identify where the feelings or longings originated from, but there is just a sense of being ill at ease, empty — the feeling of "the void".

If you become aware or have a memory of being an un-mothered child, it may now be time to heal the wounds. Cold, difficult or unsatisfactory relationships with your mother can be healed. Acknowledging that there is a problem allows for movement and then communication. Again, this is where a story can be helpful. Asking your mother questions about her own story can be a wonderful way to gain insight into her life. Women who are in their fifties may not have heard their own mother's life story. These women were born during a very difficult time in history and often they just didn't talk about it.

Maybe my generation has inherited the silence from mothers that couldn't voice their feelings? I was astounded five years ago when my mother began to talk about her life. I learned so many previously unknown family stories. Importantly her sharing gave me a much better understanding of her life and attitudes. I wish she had spoken sooner as I am sure it would have made our relationship easier. Often listening to your mother's story can stir compassion in your heart and understanding in your mind of what she has gone through in order to survive. Importantly for you, it can give you incredible insights into your own behaviour. It is possible to heal two individuals as well as a relationship by listening to one simple story.

If your mother is no longer alive but you feel the need to heal the relationship, this can be done by asking friends, neighbours or relatives about your mother. Gathering some old family snapshots can help jog memories as well as connecting you into your mother's life and maybe other women in your lineage. A personalised ritual of some kind can help with releasing withheld and unspoken words.

If you have grown up in a household where feelings were not demonstrated or expressed, and your mother's method of dealing with negative emotions was to suppress them to keep the peace, you may have inherited the same coping characteristics without even being aware of it. There is no right or wrong in this situation and certainly no need for blame; for this is the cycle of human nature. Rather than blame we can choose to come to a point of understanding that our mothers adopted these behaviours to survive as best they could at the time. But, if we have this same pattern of suppressing emotions, are we still following a pattern of behaviour? Some of us may have had mothers who, for unknown reasons, could not supply us with our emotional or soul needs. So we have grown up learning to become strong and to silently bear the inner suffering of the un-mothered child. I have known women in their sixties who have not mourned this feeling of separation until their soul has demanded it by manifesting physical symptoms or generalised emotional problems. There is a lot of grief and longing in being an un-mothered child. For some women dealing with breast cancer has provided an incentive that has provided great relief in being eventually able to talk of such things.

The following story highlights such an issue. The value of communication, of expressing these significant life events, of bringing them from the inside of one's self to the outside, seems to have a huge impact on people's general wellbeing.

Dulcie's Story

Dulcie developed breast cancer at the age of forty-eight. Her mother and sister had both died from the disease at the age of fifty. She was very frightened that when she reached fifty, she too would die.

During group discussions about these maternal patterns, Dulcie had realised that, like her mother, both her sister and herself had been *Women of Silence*. In the home as children they were well trained to "not make waves" and to "keep the peace". Their home-life was like walking on eggshells. Their dad had been an alcoholic who was easily angered and would become violent if provoked while in a drunken state. Mother's advice had always been to keep quiet and not tell anyone about what was happening at home. So the sisters secretly held on to the silence and the shame of the family problem.

Dulcie recognised the term "void". When it was described to her she indicated to the group where she felt it. She sadly placed her hand over her heart. These three women, mother and two daughters, tried to fix the family problem by denial and ignoring it, but an alcoholic father does not go away. I heard Robert Bly once describe the silence that surrounds alcoholism. He said it was like having an elephant in the living room and everyone pretends not to notice it! Dulcie lived on for nine more years but ultimately she succumbed to her breast cancer. I believe she had a peaceful and dignified death according to a friend who was with her. The friend told me a little while after that she believed that, although Dulcie died, she died a healed woman with no unfinished business to attend to.

Who Nurtures the Nurturer?

Mothering, nurturing, friendship, networking and connections are all essential components from the outside world that can nurture us.

If you have lacked the nurturing in your own early life it may be that you have matured with those early needs still unmet. Your reaction to this may be the same as many other women — the nurturing that you give out to others may be compensating for the nurturing you did not receive as a child. If this is the case you may be lacking in the personal resources necessary to maintain the constant stream of giving out. For you know the emotional pain of feeling the lack of love in your life. So, you give out, attempting to make it right, making sure everyone else's needs are met. You put yourself on the backburner and so the cycle of lack of self-care begins. This can be a very hard habit to break for you and for your family. They may have become accustomed to you doing everything for everyone and so you may have made a rod for your own back as the saying goes. If you have been diagnosed with breast cancer, this is the time for the family habit to change. A woman who had brought her twelve year old daughter along to a seminar later related to me that her daughter had said to her: "Mummy, we will be all right. You have to look after yourself now or you won't be here to look after us!"

That was the initial incentive for her change. Sometimes wanting to live for the family or to see the children grow up can be enough of a wake up call in itself to inspire healing.

Chapter Twelve

Boundaries

Healthy boundaries are a very important part of our emotional health and our general wellbeing. A boundary is a limit set by you, either by conditioning or by your intention, when you are in an empowered state. This limit, when established, determines what is identified as you and what is identified as not you. When in a dis-empowered state and your boundaries are vulnerable or non-existent, you are fatigued and suffering from what I term "energetic haemorrhage". Fritz Perls, the founder of Gestalt Therapy, used to tell people to "beware of the vibe suckers!". These are the people who can invade your space and after they leave, you feel spent and drained. In that situation an energy exchange has just taken place between you. If you feel drained, they have walked away with your energy. Although subtle, a boundary is tangible and has several key elements that enable us to recognise its existence, or lack of it.

So how do you identify your boundaries, or lack of them, and the boundaries of those around you? If you have healthy boundaries you will be an empowered person who knows and speaks your mind, has self-mastery, charisma and can very politely say "no" and mean it, without feeling guilty. Also you will not merge or get over-involved in the affairs of others, so that you take on their problems in a personal way. Your relationships will be healthy ones that build respect.

If you have a boundary issue you will notice:

- Fatigue and the associated energy drain. This is a major signal that boundaries are fragile and vulnerable. This is often experienced where there are power struggles and control issues in relationships. This is also associated with low self-esteem for women.

- An indecision, inability to focus, forgetfulness and excessive daydreaming.
- Meditation or relaxation attempts are often thwarted as you tend towards drifting, falling asleep or feeling scattered. There is often a feeling of being drained after meditation rather than feeling energised.
- You may feel jumpy and hypersensitive to external stimuli when you finish a meditation session.
- There are often feelings of "being beside yourself", disconnected, numbed and feeling as if one is functioning on automatic pilot.
- You can become overwhelmed when under pressure or, for some people, so walled off that they become unreachable.

It is my experience that people who have life-threatening illness or enduring illness of some kind inevitably have boundary issues. These are often associated with PTSD because when we become dispirited or separated out from life, this will reflect in our boundaries.

When you cannot contain your own energy within your own limits, other people can impose their will and needs upon you, and you have no resilience to keep them out of your "space". This invasion of "your space" is a part of the sense of lack of control and self-mastery evident in so many people who are unwell. The boundary has an energetic field that can be influenced by our intention. For instance becoming re-empowered and learning to say NO has a huge influence on setting this limit. For those dealing with illness, you have no doubt already appreciated the importance of creating healthy boundaries. By being bombarded by a myriad of treatment options from diagnosis to conventional and complementary/alternative options, no wonder patients are often overwhelmed, bewildered and confused. They can easily become stressed by trying too hard and too quickly to de-stress.

The new science of bio-energetic medicine can now offer some credibility to the recognition of boundaries in terms of energies. In my workshops I have devised a series of exercises that explore this area, with participants working in pairs. Women are always amazed at how and what they can sense and feel in terms of these exercises. The session is structured by sitting two people facing towards each other, eyes closed, hands outstretched but not touching. These exercises provide an experience of sensing energies around yourself and others. When I ask women to sense boundaries, I ask them to alternate between focused intent to create a boundary and no intent at all. They are always amazed at the difference in what they are able to sense and, that they actually can sense the shift. What they are sensing is the body's electromagnetic field. There is nothing highly esoteric in this really, just a natural phenomenon that most people have temporarily lost touch with in the bustle of modern day life. When we are still, focused and present, we can access this dormant ability.

Science Leads us to New Understandings

Now, we will briefly look at the science of the phenomena. Currently there exists equipment that can measure the electromagnetic field that surrounds the body. They have found that this energy can be detected up to fifteen feet away from a healthy body. I believe that this is the same energy that we can influence by intention, so that we can affect our boundary and contain, rather than disperse, energies that should bring about healing. A leader in the field of bio-electromagnetics research, Beverly Rubik, has reviewed literature that names this energy as biophoton emission. Of particular interest is the information on biophoton measurements taken by researcher Eugene Wallace using highly scientific measuring devices. He found that "more photons were measured" when people "*intended* to emit more energy". This gives credibility to the power of intention in the process of boundary creation and healing. We also know that Qigong masters have been found to emit some vital force with a very low fluctuating carrier wave. Yoga practitioners with many years of experience have also been found to emit low levels of light.

During my five months spent with Filipino healers in the late seventies, I learned that this also aligns with their theory of disease and health. These healers believe that disease can be detected in the energy field long before it is detected in the body. Hence they believe that by restoring and balancing the energy field, healing can occur. Practices of Yoga, meditation, Qigong, Tai Chi and similar disciplines are disciplines involving conscious intent. This has also been borne out by Kirlian photography, a method that records images of this energy, using very specialised equipment. I have some very impressive pictures of the hands of healers while they are healing and of hands not healing, taken on a Kirlian plate. The emissions when healing (*with intent*) are very different from those of the non-healing hand. Kirlian plates with the images of meditators' hands exhibit even patterns in the auras around the hand and fingers. The images of non-meditators exhibit quite the opposite affect.

In terms of boundaries it has been really helpful to understand the concept of intention and how it affects energy, as it is a fundamental part of boundary restoration and recovery. Our emotional state is very much reflected in the field of our boundary.

Re-Building Your Boundaries

Projected intention such as visualisation, contemplation and thought projection, either individually or combined, all play a part in creating health. There is much that you can do in reclaiming your personal power to re-build, re-create or create healthy boundaries.

There are many ways you can perceive your boundaries, such as in the sensing exercise we described earlier. You can also build an image for yourself of what you would like your boundary to be.

Sarah's Experience

Sarah was thirty six years of age. Although her face had an appearance of a much younger woman, her posture indicated a curved spine and rounded shoulders that made her look as if she had been broken through the middle of her body. In profile her backbone actually gave the appearance of an umbrella turned on its side in order to shelter a vulnerable solar plexus hidden beneath. She had grown up in a family where her father had been very overpowering. The discipline was strong, including physical punishments that were dished out for even the simplest of misdemeanors. She feared her father enormously, developed mild asthma and became the frail child. At university she studied a career course that her father had wanted her to do. She resented it, completed it, passed with honours and then married without pursuing a career.

When I met her, Sarah had two failed marriages in her wake and unresolved issues around failed pregnancies. She had developed massive allergies, verging on what we call twenty-first century allergy syndrome. Sarah was such a nice person, so helpful, polite, dutiful; the sort of person who would do anything for you if you asked even if it put her out! She was involved in lots of charitable groups and was overly emotional about many issues, over which she personally had no control. Sarah had no boundaries at all. In the past there had been an ever-present outpouring of energy but now this had been replaced by ever-present fatigue. The time had come when it was like trying to draw water from an empty well. Sarah found that she had no personal resources left to give out.

Sarah began the journey on the long road to recovering herself and creating the boundaries that perhaps, given her background, had not even existed in the past. But Sarah did recover. By using simple, small steps in reclaiming her power and by discovering how to create a protective boundary for herself, she learned how. She did this by imagining a personal invisible outer skin or buffer zone when she felt under challenge. The boundary she chose was the following and in her words:

"First I would notice in my body the signs. When I was under stress I would feel my energy running out of me like water out of a tap. So at first I would notice that this was happening to me. Then I would imagine stepping into a suit made of large bubble wrap, the type that you buy at the post office. I would imagine this like a spaceman's suit that I could put on very quickly. I would use my breath, breathing deeply and really centring myself and adjusting my posture so that I felt like a tall tree, well rooted in the ground and protected in the bubble wrap. This technique really worked for me and formed the basis of my journey back to health, allergy free. It took two years but the major shift happened when I developed my boundaries. All the remedies that I had been taking seemed to work so much better too. The work with boundaries for me was the missing link — the key to my recovery."

In my view Sarah's allergies were more based on being allergic to people and situations based on the personal trauma in her early life. Her self-esteem also improved dramatically.

When Boundaries are Restored and Health Improves

There are consequences of all actions and decisions we make, and healing is no exception. Women, who look good, feel better and who have restored their sense of self may appear to others that they no longer need help or support. It is rather a pity to state that such a problem exists; however it can be wise to prepare for it. This surprises many women and can make the practical issues of life difficult. It can especially be an issue in families where husbands, partners or children see a woman looking so well. Presuming that the crisis has passed with the possibility of normality returned, there is a premise that the family could now resume its old life. But in reality no-one ever resumes his or her old life again after the experience of cancer. So when we are looking frail and needy we may get attention and support; but be careful not to let this get in the way of what you know you need to do in terms of your recovery. This is when your newly constructed healthy boundaries can come into play. You can say NO, or can you? This becomes the test!

Using Breath and Posture

Posture very much dictates how other people read our boundaries. Thieves and muggers know this instinctively. The upright power walker is not an easy target compared to someone who is bent and frail. Body language is an unspoken dialogue that we use all the time, dictating subtle and not so subtle messages to others who we work and play with. Developing awareness of your body helps to identify your habitual body language. For instance when you notice that your shoulder is bending forwards, you can stop, take some deep breaths and be conscious of standing up straight. Even doing this at home in the mirror by alternating between the old pattern and the desired new pattern helps in developing new habits and discarding the old. The slower that you move from one form to the other apparently makes a difference to the new programming that happens in the brain.

Breath

As you are sitting here reading, just stop for one minute, and try the following. Take in a deep breath and just gently exhale sighing out the breath. Then this time take in a deep breath and exhale, deeply with the sound of Ahhhhhhh! Go back and do the first small breath again and so on. Notice the difference between the two breaths. The deeper breath almost washes down through your body rippling through the muscles. You will notice the release that goes with it. This is a good stress management method, called a circuit breaker. It is a simple tool used for helping to break the stress cycle and can be used anywhere at anytime. The spin off is that it also helps to bring you more *present* to your body, more aware and into your own space. It sounds simplistic, but breath enlivens the body.

Frequently, repairing or recreating your personal boundary requires the presence of another person. This person can assist you to become more aware of your body and recognize your boundary issues. Many therapists offer to work with you on a one-to-one basis or, alternatively, you could attend a workshop. Once you experience what is meant by the term boundaries, and have learned to apply this information to yourself, you then can self-pace your boundary work in your own time. For the most effective boundary work, incorporate mindfulness and focus, with someone to assist you, into noticing the changes in your body which, then, makes you more aware of these changes.

If you choose to experiment to understand and recreate boundaries on your own, I highly recommend the book *Boundaries and Relationships* by Dr Charles Whitford.

Chapter Thirteen

Imagining Health – Affirmations and Imagery for Healing

When we are ready to make plans and put them into action, we often need a mechanism to break with our old habits and establish new ones. This is where affirmations and imagery can be so useful.

What are Affirmations?

All affirmations are commands. They are words of power. Affirmations are a simple, easily learned means that you can use to move stagnant old belief systems and to stimulate new patterns of positive action. They are a great way to advance from feeling stuck to acting positively and effectively. Affirmations have been a healing tool for thousands of years. Probably the oldest and most accessible place to find them in quantity is in the Bible, particularly in the sections related to healing.

An affirmation is usually a short sentence that summarises an important goal you have set yourself. To work best they need to be precise and usually they are repeated silently, out loud, or even better, sung with passion! The more you work with them, the more potent they become. Used effectively, affirmations can be invaluable for establishing new and more life-enhancing belief patterns.

How Do Affirmations Work?

Affirmations can assist our intentions into action! When our thoughts and intentions are clear, and focused and directed through an affirmation with conviction and certainty, then there is a high probability that the desired end result will be brought about. Experience suggests that those affirmations that are made at a deep level of self, those made with utter certainty; are those that bear fruit easily and will have spiritual merit. To make that type of affirmation requires clarity and confidence. These are qualities that are the natural products of quiet meditation. They can also be helped by open communication, the telling of stories and wise counsel. Once you have the clarity and confidence, your affirmation will go to work easily.

But what if you are not clear and confident yet? This is the time when using affirmations can be such a useful tool in your healing programme, particularly if you are having difficulty changing an aspect of your life that you need or want to change. It helps to believe in what you are doing as well as having the *possibility* of your changes being attainable.

In the chapter on how conditioning in early life affects our behaviour, we used the term "premature cognitive commitment" to explain how we encode certain behavioural patterns. Affirmations work by making a new pattern of "commitment" thereby establishing new belief systems to live by. A friend often talks about his own introduction to affirmations some twenty years ago. Continued ill health was really getting Lionel down and he was looking hard for answers, when someone told him about the power of affirmations. Almost every part of his body was affected by various ailments, so he decided that he would *sing* to his body organs all through the day. He made up a little tune using these words: "My liver is lovely, my duodenum is delightful, my pancreas is perfect, my bowel is beautiful" and so on. This may sound cute and strange, but Lionel had a hundred per cent success rate in returning to full health and enjoyed himself in the process.

Some years ago, a patient had a very difficult time dealing with an aggressive ulcerating carcinoma of the breast that had been unresponsive to treatment. Mavis was very enthusiastic about the use of affirmations and decided to empower her healing response by applying them to healing the ulcer. In an almost ritual way she gently applied herbal ointment onto the ulcerated area, affirming each time "Only good, healthy cells can live here — no-one else is welcome!". During the day Mavis would gently place her hand over the area and repeat the same words. Combined with her enthusiastic approach to meditation during which time she also affirmed her healing, Mavis managed to heal the ulcerated skin within three weeks!

The process Mavis used to increase her healing response is known as imprinting. She had chosen her goal very clearly and then creatively worked towards it by establishing a belief in the area's ability to heal. Her statement of intention was precise and direct and Mavis was very clear about her goal. Importantly, that goal was stated in the present tense. These are all principles that are necessary to make affirmations work for you. Simply stated, there are three basic principles for the effective use of affirmations. They require words in the present tense, used in the first person and they need to be target or goal orientated.

How to Make and Use Affirmations

Experience tells me that those affirmations that people design for themselves work best. Only you have a familiarity with the way you think, sense and understand the world and the symbols in life that are important to you. Also, during your life you have created your own storehouse of knowledge and memory to draw upon. Therefore you may prefer to design your own affirmations.

Many of my patients have had their creativity ignited and have composed some fun affirmations. The following ditty is sung to the tune of "I am a fine musician" (similar to Hayden's *Surprise Symphony*):

Now I am a positive person, I practise every day,
My cancer's disappearing, soon be gone away.
Now I am a positive person, I sing it in the shower,
For I'm positively blooming, like a little flower.
Now I am a positive person, I practise it with joy,
I look forward to my meal times and always say "oh boy!"
Now I am a positive person, I love this world we're in.
I love my fellow neighbour, myself and all my kin.

Suggestions for Creating and Writing Your Own Affirmations

1. Affirmations need to be stated in the first person, in the present tense, as if they are already achieved. So they need to begin with words like "I am" or "I have". They need to be in the "now".
2. The goal, the desired result of the affirmation, needs to be stated in a way that is brief, precise, accurate and complete.
3. Compose your affirmations with positive meaning. For example, rather than using "I am not a negative person" try the positive expression of "I am a positive person, now".
4. Give yourself an open-ended time frame, i.e. don't pressure yourself to have a result by a certain time.
5. Use direct language — after all, affirmations are words of power or commands to yourself.
6. Use precise language, being specific in your outcome. A direct, focused and precise affirmation can make powerful shifts in your belief system.
7. Set realistic goals. The object is to assist you with the replacement or transformation of old belief systems into new belief systems. If your goals are too way out or

unrealistic, your self-doubt will immediately discard them. Base your goals on the best possible result that you can imagine and believe in.

8. Sometimes saying the affirmation by really looking at yourself in the mirror can be helpful. If you don't like what you see, maybe more work is needed on self-worth and self-esteem.

Dealing with Negative "Self Talk": The Saboteur

Hopefully during the healing process you will begin to be aware of messages, the "self talk" messages that play in your head throughout the day and create the background of your life. Often they sound as if you were listening to an internal, repetitive tape recorder. These messages that we give ourselves in the privacy of our own head, twenty four hours each day, can make a difference to the effectiveness of our affirmations and imagery.

For example, if you meditate for one hour each day where you use your affirmations and imagery, but demonstrate worry and fear fuelled by negative "self talk" for the other twenty three hours, you cannot expect a wonderful result! These tools of healing cannot be used as you would use a drug i.e. take one dose and forget about it. The process of healing requires observation and awareness of ourselves and our habitual thought patterns throughout the day.

Negative self-talk such as "you're not good enough"; "you always do that the wrong way"; "you can't heal" etc, tend to plague your thoughts at first. You will need to catch yourself before you fall, replacing the negative affirmations with positive ones. For example, "I always do things the right way now" and "I am worthy of healing now".

Initially you may find it difficult working with affirmations in that you will be making a statement in the present tense about an event or goal that has not happened yet. This, at first, may seem paradoxical or confusing. But if we begin to understand the way that our mind works, the way it learns and relearns, affirmations do make sense and can be incorporated into our lives as powerful healing accessories. When I was very ill and experiencing tremendous pain after my ileostomy (the epidural only worked on one side of my body!), I had learned a short phrase from Sogyal Rimpoche that states: "All things pass and this too will pass". I added to the phrase "Tomorrow, the pain will be less". This affirmation was very helpful during the post anaesthesia delirium.

You are not fooling yourself or being dishonest by affirming something that has not yet happened, because you have the intention that it will happen. The key issue is that deep within yourself, you have made a fundamental decision that it is time to change. You may not know yet how it will happen but your intention to change is clear and definite. That intention, combined with words of power, will begin to make a change or a shift. In this process you are affirming the result you require. Once inner movement commences, the process of transformation begins to flow. By using affirmations, we are redirecting our attention, choosing a new belief and expecting the changes to occur.

Prayer: Spiritual Intention in Action

Prayer involves conscious intent. It is concentrating your thoughts or questions using fine-tuning, powered by intention. Prayer is asking the question and meditation is waiting for the answer. Sometimes it helps if you have a belief system; but I have known many people to be affected by prayer at a distance, without a belief and without them knowing that they were being prayed for! There is a lot of mystery in healing too! Sometimes prayer can be used as a one-to-one local healing session such as in the practice of laying on of hands. Prayer or touch with intention is very powerful indeed. At other times prayer can be used for distant or non-local healing when the person who is thought about, does not have to be present. The following abstract on

155

the results of prayer was published in the respected and conventional *Southern Medical Journal* in 1988 (USA). The study demonstrates that there can be a marked effect on recovery through prayer power. The following is just one of many such studies that highlight a closing of the gap between science and healing!

Randolph Byrd MD, arranged for prayer healing to be sent to 192 patients on a coronary care unit, while another 201 patients served as control. This was done with a double blind design, where neither the patients nor the treating nor the evaluating physicians knew which patients were sent the healing and which were not. The patients were randomly assigned to either of these groups and no significant differences were noted between the groups on many variables. *Highly significant effects were found in the treated group (the ones receiving the prayer healing), in which there were lower incidences of intubation/ventilation, use of antibiotics, cardiopulmonary arrest, congestive heart failure, pneumonia, and the use of diuretics.*

Imagery: Pictures and Symbols from the Soul

Affirmations combine powerfully with the use of imagery. Affirmations involve the repetition of words. Imagery involves the generation of images in the mind that can be sensed or visualised as symbols or pictures. The techniques are well recognised by both patients and health workers who regularly see and experience the benefits. To begin it is important to state that not everyone is a suitable candidate for using imagery. Some patients really worry about not being able to image, sense, smell or define a symbol that represents their cancer. If this describes you, do not place too much emphasis on imagery as a part of your healing journey. By all means have a try; but if it is not for you just concentrate on deep relaxation, meditation and mindfulness.

Try this exercise right now. Close your eyes and imagine a place that you have been to that makes you feel terrific. For example, take yourself off to an exotic location. Imagine a sapphire blue sea, blinding white sands and swaying palms. Imagine that you are stretched out on the sand, feeling the hot sun warming your skin. Feel the liquid, tropical breeze gently massaging you. Come back to reality. This exercise will give you some indication whether imagery will work for you. Images generate feelings about how your body can be. Just think for a moment what you felt, or noticed, when you imagined yourself on that beach. For example, did your breathing pattern change? Did you notice a change in your body temperature? Was there a change in your state of mind?

Orthodox Western medical science struggles to come to terms with the mechanisms that would explain how these processes work and their desire is to look for tangible reasons why. The observable fact for those who work in this field is that these techniques do in fact, work. While some aspects of this mechanism may remain mysterious, we certainly can now understand a good deal about how images work, since the birth of PNI (psycho-neuro-immunology). The limbic brain can communicate, receive and decipher symbols and images and use them to dialogue with various cellular activities in the body; possibly via the receptors on cells. For instance the receptors on immune cells are likely to be the conduit.

If we look to history and the ancient healing practices of Shamanism, we will see that they have used the power of imagery in healing for thousands of years. All the great religions of the world have used combinations of imagery, icons and prayer to strengthen or change belief systems and to bring about healing.

Defining Images

From my own experience I have found that there are two distinctly different ways that we can use the power of imagery in our healing. We can use **creative** imagery or **spontaneous** imagery.

157

Creative Imagery

First, we can induce or create an image in our mind by linking into thoughts of a past experience. Choosing to think about a happy past event will bring back memories in the form of pictures in our mind. We may associate other senses, such as sounds, fragrances or sensations with these memories.

You can get a clear idea of how this type of imagery works and how it affects the body by this simple experiment. In this thought-connected image you can keep your eyes open if you wish.

Simply imagine a lemon — oval shaped, bright yellow in colour and freshly picked from the tree. Imagine holding the lemon, and have a sense of its fragrance. Now, in your mind, take it into the kitchen and carefully cut it, allowing the bitter juice to flow out. Imagine then dipping your finger into the juice and tasting its tart flavour. By the end of this experiment your salivary glands are likely to have contracted and there will be excess saliva in your mouth. The words have created inner pictures that stirred a memory of a previous experience, and in doing so, produced a result in the body.

This experiment gives us direct experience of the brain-body connection and how it works as an interwoven, integrated system. This is related to a real image based on previous knowledge and experience. There is therefore a reference point for the use of this kind of image in healing. But images and symbols must be chosen carefully lest you image something that will not be helpful to your healing; for example imaging your tumour as a snowball rolling down a mountain! We all know that this type of snowball grows bigger as it travels. However a single snow ball thrown, which then disintegrates and whose fragments turn into water vapour, to be evaporated by the rays of the sun, is a different image.

Whilst choosing to create images like this can have many beneficial effects, to me it is an image forced rather than intuited. Therefore it has a realm of fantasy about it. It is not my preferred type of imagery for use in healing. What I do prefer is to use the potent images that spontaneously come to us in a dream or meditation, or even in our day-to-day thoughts.

Spontaneous Imagery

This is not a consciously induced process. There are images that can arise spontaneously at any time, but are more likely to appear during meditation, moments of quiet reverie or during dreams. These are profound images direct from our psyche, our unconscious and perhaps even our subconscious.

It seems likely that these images are transported in some kind of symbolic biochemical manner via a neural network that links our brain and body. Imagery is one of the key pathways that enables activation of this brain–body (mind–body) connection. Our memories, perceptions and emotions register as images in our mind and are then translated to the body. The body acts like a receptor; it accepts and responds to the messages received. When these messages are received over long periods of time, they can begin to change our body chemistry by, for example, giving cells the correct directions or bringing about homeostasis. Imagery could be described as a two way coding process.

Because the mind–body connection is a two-way communication system, spontaneous images can be generated in reverse. In other words, images can flow from the body to the mind. This communication can inform and report if there are abnormalities that need to be brought to our attention. In the same way it can provide a solution to a problem. This solution may be in the form of a symbol which the brain (mind) can receive and interpret.

Imagery has many useful attributes for women dealing with breast cancer. It can help with physical healing on many levels — by directly dealing with the tumour itself, by accelerating recovery from surgery or alleviating the side effects of toxic treatments. Emotionally, imagery can help you, very effectively, to come to terms with fear and anxiety about treatment regimes. So, how do we do it?

There are three methods of imagery that we can use.

1. Literal Imagery

You can use images that you create in your mind, directed by thought or intention, to achieve the desired result. It seems that at least 75% of people can create this type of image when they choose to. As stated before if you are not one of the 75% don't worry and just focus on what you **can** do well.

This first type of imagery is known as literal imagery. One very useful way of using this type of imagery is when you recreate situations in your mind as they might happen to you in real life — such as a trip to the dentist or a visit to the doctor for injections that you may not find pleasant. In the safety of your own lounge, or a therapist's room, you can then deal with any associated fears in your mind, far from the area where treatment would occur. Using imagery, you rehearse; you practise a favoured outcome. Many patients have found help using this technique in dealing with fears associated with chemotherapy or radiotherapy. Importantly, this type of imagery is practised in a state of relaxation. If in doubt contact a therapist to assist you. The following scenario is what you might expect from such a session. Once you are feeling calm and relaxed, the scenes associated with your memories of chemotherapy are replayed in your mind. You run through the sequence of images until you reach the point where your feeling of being at ease, being comfortable, is lost. At that point the therapist can take the patient back to a place where calm is restored. During the next session steps are taken to go a little further, keeping within the patient's comfort zone. A skilled practitioner working with imagery in this way can improve a patient's quality of life dramatically, for often, when fear is dissolved, many side effects lessen dramatically.

If you are dealing with breast cancer and you feel that this type of imagery could benefit you, seek the support of either a group working with imagery, or an individual practitioner for guidance on what will work best for you. Another way to use literal imagery is at the end of each meditation session, when you can create a positive image of yourself in good health. A photograph of a particularly happy time when you were radiant can be useful to reinforce this. I often recommend that one or several such photos be kept at key places, so they can be savoured throughout the day. Such photographs will stimulate good memories and positive feelings.

When the process required in order to achieve your goal is clear, literal images are the best to use. Another woman who used this process was a pathologist named Maggie. She attended a residential programme and was keen to learn the art of imagery to deal with her myeloid leukaemia. Of course Maggie's occupation stood her in good stead to be able to literally image what was going on at a cellular level in her blood. She was able to imagine her cells with great precision and had a fun time with her healing, using as her mainstays, meditation and literal imagery.

However, most of us do not have the biochemical knowledge to carry out such imagery accurately enough, and with literal imagery, accuracy is vital. So, what do we do when we do not have a clear, literal image of what we want to happen?

2. Symbolic Imagery

To me this is the most interesting and extraordinary type of imagery. Symbolic images may appear spontaneously or we may choose to create them. Symbols are ideal when we have a clear intention of what we want to happen, but do not have a clear idea of how to make it happen. Because the literal process of healing is so complicated, very few people can use literal imagery accurately for healing. But they can use symbols to convey the conscious intention to the

161

subconscious, in a way that it will be acted upon. Symbolic imagery can be a way of directing the subconscious healing processes into focused, effective action.

Symbols for the healing process can be consciously chosen, but they seem to be even more powerful when they arise spontaneously. Karen's story demonstrates the power of spontaneous symbolism.

Although Karen was having chemotherapy for her particularly aggressive breast cancer, the prognosis was poor. But, importantly for our example here, the fact that her images came to her spontaneously was a key factor. She told me that, as if on a video screen inside her head, one day during a meditation there appeared a clear image of this huge bunch of grapes; nothing else! The image stayed for several minutes, until she finished her session. At our next consultation, she asked about the significance of this strange image, particularly as she did not even like grapes. She was finding the image quite distracting, but it would not go away. At this point Karen even questioned whether or not meditation was for her! However, the significance of this image for her healing was immediately obvious to me and upon explanation, she became quite excited. The idea of symbolic imagery was quite new to her. She had tried to make fantasy pictures in her head before, but it seemed to only distract her from the relaxation she aimed for. Hence she had felt that imagery was not for her and so had given it up.

This image of a bunch of grapes clearly was symbolic of her breast cancer. At a cellular level, the grape skins were symbolic of the tough membranes around her tumour.

So, with a new view of how this imagery could help her, at each meditation session, and always in a profoundly relaxed state, Karen would visualise and peel each grape. By imagining peeling the grape skins away, Karen was symbolically assisting in the process of exposing the tumour to the action of the chemotherapy and her natural immunity. But the next frustration was that each time she went back, the grapes had grown a new skin that seemed tougher and harder to peel.

Karen's image demonstrated how healing might take place in her body! Such is the body's innate wisdom. From a scientific point of view, it is well known that tumour density is one reason why chemotherapy has trouble gaining access to and penetrating a tumour's core. Tumours can also make their own chemicals that help to screen out chemotherapy over time. During this process the membrane or dense outer layer can become more impenetrable to the drugs that are used. In Karen's case, there was an amazing similarity between what was going on in her breast tumour in reality, and how the body–mind had communicated the symbol. In fact her results indicated that the tumour had become resistant to the chemotherapy drugs.

To conclude Karen's story, she became enthusiastically creative and changed her imagery to only peeling one cluster of grapes at a time, paying attention to being really thorough. As well, in her mind, she nipped off small twigs from the grape clusters. As a result, the grapes began to rot, and in her imagination she carried the debris to the compost heap and burned them. The result was that Karen managed to shrink the tumour significantly. She was suddenly responding to her treatment, much to the surprise of her oncologist who had advised her to stop the chemotherapy. So improved was she, that the tumour was able to be de-bulked surgically, which had not been possible previously due to its extent.

Karen survived for some time, but the death of two patients with whom she had become close friends, distressed her greatly. Her health rapidly declined and her tumour recurred virulently soon after. She died within a matter of weeks after the death of her friends.

You may find that symbolic imagery will manifest spontaneously or as a result of contemplation. However, if you need to consciously choose an image, use ones that come to you naturally. It is my recommendation that you do not use someone else's images for your needs. It is likely that their body will be communicating what is right for them, not necessarily what is right for you.

With any type of imagery, if you have been using images geared at destroying the cancer, you also must pay attention to the eradication process of any debris that remains. Find a creative way to remove it from the body.

Finally, as a purely practical consideration, you need a way to make sure that the images you are using are accurate and complete. A good way to check out the entire process of your imagery is to draw it out on paper, including the mechanism of the "clean up team". If you are unsure of your images, consult a therapist working in this field. However, many women have told me that after drawing their image, it became obvious to them what was required. Husbands and families also often came up with helpful suggestions about how to put the image to work in the body.

Like all new skills, there can be some useful learning to do, as well as experimenting for yourself. Seek guidance from therapists who have had some experience with imagery and cancer. With meditation, you may find tapes helpful to induce a physically relaxed state, and in the stillness, either use your image consciously or allow a space for an image to come spontaneously.

Some essential helpful hints for symbolic imagery are:

1. Imagine the cancer as weak, confused, disorganised and vulnerable.
2. Perceive your body's defences as being organised, powerful, purposeful and effective.
3. Images used should be vivid, clear and positive. Use all your senses in the process.
4. It is to your advantage to image your medical treatments as potent and effective against the cancer.
5. Remember to do the "clean up" process after your imagery.

3. Abstract Imagery

Abstract imagery involves the use of universal symbols. For healing, the images of flowing water and white light seem to be extremely helpful images to use. They are simple to understand and powerful in their mechanism. These images seem to have a wide appeal to women and can be tremendously helpful during treatment. For example, imagining your chemotherapy being administered as an intravenous drip containing pure liquid white light that flows through the veins and arteries into the tumours, has been a very effective image for many women dealing with breast cancer. Fresh flowing pure water also can work well. To get you started I recommend that you use an audio tape or CD with a simple abstract guided image and music. Both water and light are very safe and pleasant images to use.

What to do if Dark and Negative Images Appear

Like a bad dream or a nightmare, negative images can occasionally appear. Sometimes these can be very potent and a little scary especially if you are not expecting them. However, I have found them to be the exception rather than the rule. Also, I do know that the message will almost always have some significance for you. This is a time to consult the experts such as a psychotherapist or Jungian analyst. I strongly suggest that you do not ignore persistent negative images. Sometimes the issues we have screened from consciousness, that appear shadowy and dark, can be the very ones that will lead us into the light.

How Do You Perceive Your Breast Cancer? A Special Use for Imagery

How you personally view or perceive your breast cancer will have an influence on all your therapeutic approaches. The three questions that I ask of all my patients are:

1. How do you perceive your cancer?
2. What does it mean to you?
3. How has it affected you?

The answer to these questions may help you to find an image or a symbol. The following is a list of women's different perceptions of what breast cancer represented or symbolised for them.

- A nuisance.
- An opportunity for change.
- A parasite.
- An enemy.
- A challenge.
- Death.
- Isolation and emptiness.
- A part of them.
- Punishment.

As you can see from the list above, the approaches for women who view their breast cancer so differently will need to cater for their individuality. These women could all have the same type of cancer, be treated with the same type of chemotherapy and yet, depending on how they viewed their illness, they could all respond differently.

The patient who viewed cancer as death has probably lost her spirit and her reason to be. The best that a therapist may be able to do, is to help her die well. Contrast this with the patient who views her cancer as an opportunity to change. Such a woman is already displaying possibility thinking and is likely to do well with whatever modality of treatment she chooses.

It is important to realize that it is possible to change a negative image into a positive and more beneficial one. This can be done with outside help or by the patient's own determination. There are a lot of possibilities.

A good therapist can give you techniques and tools to help you along the way, but they cannot restore your will to live.

Only you can make the decision to do that. You can choose to heal with zeal. The only real freedom we have in life is how we choose to respond to it. You can choose to respond actively and positively to breast cancer. By doing so you are virtually assured of improving your quality of life and there is good evidence that you increase your chances of survival significantly.

Chapter Fourteen

Dealing with Emotional Healing and Menopause

It is important to include the experience of menopause when we discuss emotional healing and breast cancer. As women, we are influenced in behaviour and function for all of our lives by our hormones. When they are balanced and performing in the way that they were intended to, we experience wellbeing. When they are out of balance we are out of balance. Our emotional state therefore is very reflective of our hormonal state and vice versa. In relation to breast cancer, hormone treatments that block the receptors on breast cancer cells have probably been the most successful of all the breast cancer treatments, with the least side effects. The growing understanding of hormones and their relationship to breast cancer may be one of the keys to finding future breast cancer cell growth inhibitors which will work for many more breast cancers than the ones that are oestrogen positive.

Not only can we affect hormones by our behaviours and behaviours by our hormones, but one of the biggest threats to our health today are hormones in the environment and the food chain. When we regularly and unknowingly ingest these substances the situation becomes more complicated. Many popular chemicals used in both the past and present are known as hormone disrupters and many of these chemicals can mimic hormones such as oestrogen in our body. This is a reality of living the way we do. Eating certified organically grown produce must help a lot; but the other pollutants may be an insidious occurrence that is beyond our control.

My original training was in herbal medicine, nutrition and natural therapies. However over the years I think that it has become more difficult to treat clients with hormonally related problems such as breast cancer. The best outcome seems to be the combination of using natural therapies to support any hormonal treatment and/or chemotherapy. Hormonal blocking drugs do work well in many cases. I believe this is due to the environmental issues. Some of this contact with chemicals probably happened a generation ago to our mothers and has carried over in the altered genetic substance that we inherit. This section should give you some food for thought and some understanding of the processes of one of our most profound hormonal shifts, menopause.

Menopause is usually a natural transition time in a woman's life, signifying major hormonal shifts. It can also be induced by cancer therapy treatments such as radiation therapy, chemotherapy and surgical removal of the ovaries. In the natural development of menopause there is a slow progression towards transition which may involve a period of up to ten years of adaptation time as a woman moves into the next phase of her life. On the whole, it is quite possible for a woman to experience this change without too much drama. However, a woman's perception of what might be, her expectations, can cause significant worries.

In current Western society there are many unhelpful myths surrounding menopause. The medical system commonly approaches menopause as a pathological condition involving a shriveling of the reproductive system. Contrast this with the Native American and Chinese cultures, which have no equivalent word for menopause in their language. In days gone by, women from these cultures whose periods had ceased, were elevated to the status of a wise one or elder honoured for their life's knowledge. In our own culture, if they do not buy into the "menopause myth", women with healthy bodies, minds and spirits can move into menopause with knowledge, understanding and minimal symptoms.

However, there is no doubt that the scenario is quite different for women who experience an artificially created menopause. Invariably for them the changes can be rapid and dramatic. The reasons for artificial menopause in today's society can be many. In the early days of surgery, the removal of a woman's ovaries and uterus was more common, as it was not realised that the organs of reproduction had extensive hormonal value in the body. Today it is known that there are literally hundreds of different cellular reactions of which oestrogen is an imperative and deemed to be an integral part. Other hormones that you need to be aware of are progesterone, androgens such as testosterone and prolactin; the hormone involved in breast development and lactation. A sudden partial or total removal, as well as the chemical closing down of our reproductive system, can have drastic effects on our health and wellbeing.

Today it is known that some tumours of the breast can be stimulated to grow in the presence of oestrogen. These are called oestrogen receptive tumours. You might recognise this as the ER+ that could be on some of your test results. A term commonly used for these types of tumours is that they are hormone-dependent. One medical response to this hormonal problem and its relation to breast cancer has been to shut down the hormonal production from the ovaries by surgical removal or by chemical means. Occasionally, this is done using radiotherapy.

Surgical removal of the uterus is called an hysterectomy. A bilateral oophorectomy is the removal of two ovaries and unilateral oophorectomy is the removal of one ovary. If you are recommended to have reproductive surgery such as this, or already have had it performed, be sure that you are clear exactly what type of procedure you have undergone. Preferably ask your surgeon or gynaecologist for a complete explanation on paper. It often amazes me that many of my female cancer patients are totally unaware of the nature of surgical procedures that have been performed on them. There have been a variety of reasons, such as that they have failed to ask at all or failed to ask the right questions. Typically they did not have the procedure explained to them in language that they could understand or they were too shocked to take any information on board, despite an adequate explanation.

I have found it quite incredible that women could have such a sketchy view of what had happened to such an important part of their body. Maybe this too is linked to *Women of Silence*.

Instant Menopause

Surgical menopause creates a "shock" to the body, due to the ovarian blood supply being suddenly severed. Having your uterus removed is enough of a shock, but when both ovaries and uterus are removed, the shock to the body is enormous. This surgery creates instant menopause, a process remember, that would normally have a ten year prelude. I have seen women as young as twenty-five years old who, not only have had to deal with breast cancer, but also premature menopause.

Naturally this requires major readjustments in many areas of your life, especially in the areas of relationship, sexuality and emotions. It is imperative to communicate with husbands, partners or lovers and, if possible, encourage them to attend consultations with you so that they can ask questions. Self-esteem can suffer enormously and many emotional difficulties can arise. Usually around the time of diagnosis and surgery there is so much happening that not a great deal of attention is given to problems that may arise at a later date. It takes a mature relationship and a courageous woman to deal with many of these problems. Treatments are often unkind in their side effects and hair loss and nausea can diminish a woman's self-esteem and libido even more. Many women have commented that the shock of this instant menopause made them feel very much out of time or synchronicity with life, relationships and themselves generally.

Menopause would normally be viewed as a key transition time in a woman's life. At this time, as with PMS or at other times of major hormonal shifts in the body, there will be an emotional response. Many women falsely believe a myth that the ovaries cease to function at all at menopause, rather than the fact that the ten year transition period is by definition exactly what it is — a transition of hormonal change, not a cessation. Whether menopause is induced or natural, this process can be likened to a change in electrical current. If it occurs naturally and gradually, it gives a woman time to adjust to this new way of being and thinking. There may be, for some women, symptoms indicating that this process of change is underway. These can manifest as hot flushes that are nothing more than surges in oestrogen levels — like a boost of energy. They are not to be feared. Renaming them "power surges" in a flow of alternating current may help you to view them in a new way. Night sweats and mood swings are possible and for women with their reproductive system intact, heavy bleeding at times can occur. All of these are symptoms. They are not an illness, just symptoms of changeover time.

The more "stressed out" and fatigued you are at the time surrounding menopause and the more you have lived your life for others, the more symptoms you are likely to experience. I recommend that women find for themselves, either a gynaecologist, a general practitioner, homeopath or **qualified** natural health practitioner with a special interest in women's health — someone whom you can trust and consult if any symptoms of menopause seem excessive. You may need another health professional but make sure that they are in contact with your key oncologist. It is worth finding out about such doctors long before the time when you may need their services. Ask around and get personal recommendations from your friends. If you are dealing with a serious illness such as breast cancer, your choice of appropriate doctor may not only be life saving; but proper hormonal management can make a real difference to your quality of life. If your libido has "flatlined" and this is of concern to you or your partner, be sure to discuss this with your doctor. If you do not feel satisfied with their advice, seek the advice of a recommended sex therapist. On a practical note there are many non-hormonal lubricants available that makes intercourse more pleasurable, as one of the unfortunate side effects of menopause, whatever way it is induced, is a dry vagina. This can become quite sore and painful even if you are not sexually active. A natural therapist or pharmacist should be able to help you with this.

For women whose menopausal time is on "fast forward" all of these normal transitional symptoms are manifested almost instantaneously, with no preparation or adjustment period. Again it surprises me how many women do not discuss these inconveniences in their body functions and their sexuality with their doctors. Some women accept symptoms that would send most of us running for help on one hand and running away from our men folk on the other. Why do women suffer in silence at a time when relationship, closeness, warmth and intimacy are more needed than ever before in their life? This can be a very tough time for partners and can create problems within the relationship. The loss of a breast may not only threaten womanhood but may also involve the problems associated with having to deal with an instant and early menopause. All of this can strike a blow at the heart of even the toughest survivor personality.

In my work I deal with these problems all the time, and interestingly, these topics are guarded in conversation during consultations, virtually never mentioned in a mixed group, yet always launched into with relish and sometimes even with a bawdiness in "women only" groups! Amidst the safety of the group environment, where sisterhood and sharing of their membership and initiation into the *scar clan* is openly felt, women can at last feel free to share and question with understanding ears and hearts. Some women have openly shared the fact that they have never enjoyed their sexuality anyway and that now they have an excuse not to feel guilty in denying their husbands' sexual demands. This comment often receives a nervous and understanding chuckle from other group members and usually someone pipes up with a comment like "Yeah, I don't have to pretend I've got a headache any more!" Many women in these groups comment how they feel that their sex life in marriage has been more out of duty despite the fact that they love their husbands and this has always been a conflict for them. These women often relate how they grew up with parents who were quite reserved or strict regarding sexuality. The great thing is that they are talking about it. The majority of women that I see, grew up in the era of more permissive sexuality and feminism. Yet somehow the old patterning and conditioning of sexuality in the home environment can over-rule. Don't be embarrassed to ask and find solutions.

For other women, the story can be rosier. Certainly for some, breast cancer can cause their relationships to become deeper and more intimate and honest than ever. Often these are the women who have experienced long term loving relationships with a genuine level of care from their partners. Often for them, however, they have grown apart without noticing. A diagnosis of cancer has been a strong wake-up call for both of them about the preciousness of good relationship. They quickly embrace what my programme has to offer, need little motivation, get on with it and enjoy their new life as Pauline's story shows us. It is fair to say, however, that in people who I see regularly, these couples are more the exception than the rule.

Pauline's Story

"I had a mastectomy and no further treatment. Two years later I was diagnosed as having extensive secondaries in my spine, skull, ribs and right leg. After three weeks of radiotherapy I was put on Tamoxifen. I attended a residential self-help course with my husband where we had an intensive week of meditation, positive thinking, looking at diet and generally how to live well with a life-threatening illness. We returned home and put it all into practice. We took up meditation, became vegetarians and my husband gave up his managerial position to work part-time as a consultant so that he could spend more time with me. I had given up my job straight after the secondaries were diagnosed."

Later Pauline wrote in a letter:

"I saw the oncologist yesterday. Apparently he is a world authority on prostate and testicular cancer, so here's hoping he knows as much about bones as balls! A normally emotionless, but articulate man (it seems to go with the job), he had a lot of trouble disguising his excitement (he even looked as though he was gearing up for a hug!) and was almost reduced to apoplexy when he saw my scan. According to him the report had underestimated the dramatic changes since the last scan. He was amazed at my improvement since then. He even gave me most of the credit as he felt the treatment was insignificant compared with my ability to manage it all. I have just returned from a holiday on Lord Howe Island where I had been hill climbing. Not bad for someone who was told that bush-walking would be off my list of activities.

The dividends have paid off, as I went into remission for sixteen months. My last two bone scans in February and June showed a slight progression of the disease, so I have been placed on another hormone preparation called Farlutal. I continue to keep very well. I am mobile and have little pain. I walk my dog on the beach daily, do my own gardening, (I gave the housework away a long time ago!), meditate daily and go to hydrotherapy and swim nearly a kilometre twice per week. I am currently planning a trip to Europe. So there is life and indeed a life quality after secondaries."

Menopause: Revealing a Thin Veil between Two Worlds

You may remember or still be aware of the times that are commonly called premenstrual syndrome or PMS. You may still feel emotionally sensitive even if you have had an induced menopause. Comments are often made such as, "Look out, its hormone time again, better duck for cover". Or your husband looks at you in amazement and says, "You must have your period or you are out of your mind!". You may have even been branded a "lunatic!" which, as we have seen already, is an accurate statement, given that the moon's lunar cycles are related to women's cycles! Comedian Loretta La Roche has a very fun way of re-framing menopause. She says that she had a T shirt made that said "I'm out of oestrogen and I have a gun!".

Heightened emotional activity and sensitivity are normal in women at times of hormonal shifts. Menopause is not the only time in our lives that we have changeover of hormones — it has been occurring all of your life if you are a woman. Many women have experienced hot flushes, well before the time of menopause, because of major hormonal shifts. The first fifty years or so of a woman's life is like sitting on a see-saw of hormonal shifts and adjustments. The joy of being female!

Cultural perceptions and myths, along with a medical profession that is trained to believe that women have a reproductive system that needs fixing, are all factors that need to be looked at in the areas of women's healthcare.

There are two major aspects of our lives that seem to affect our hormonal patterns. These are the effects of prolonged and negative stress in our lives, and how truly we are living our lives according to the tune of our own souls. At all of these times of cyclic change, we as women become highly sensitive to any inconsistencies in our lives. Chemotherapy can really highlight this time even if it has not induced premature menopause. I believe that what happens, at these times of hormonal flux, is an opportunity for women to take time out, be still and listen to the needs of the inner self. In the old days women went to the red tent to spend time with other women, rest and discover the secrets of "women's business". Women were much better prepared for womanhood in some ways during those days.

Emotional Healing and Menopause

At the time of menopause it is as if the veil between our two worlds of existence suddenly becomes thinner. Many women describe this as a time when the intellect and intuition seem to face each other. At this time we can become emotionally hypersensitive or for some women it can become a time of depression. The closer that a woman is paying attention to her soul life in balance with her physical life, the healthier she will be and the easier her menopausal time will be. It is highly likely that at this time, anything that is not right in your life, will come closer to your attention. There is no substitute for effective stress management, self-care and taking time for yourself.

Treatments and Their Effects

Tamoxifen is a man-made hormone and is the most used and well known of the treatments for breast cancer. It is an anti-oestrogen that works by binding oestrogen receptors on breast cancer cells. This in turn can either slow down the growth rate of breast cancer cells or retard them completely. Although taking Tamoxifen won't stop your body producing oestrogen, it can effectively stop cancer sells from using it. If you are pre-menopausal Tamoxifen may induce irrregular periods and if you nearer to menopause, it is likely that your periods will cease. Sometimes the drug can increase your weight, so plan for this by making lifestyle changes. There are many other side effects; but most are manageable. Your oncologist should advise you. If you are taking Tamoxifen ask your clinic for a pamphlet about the drug so that you are informed, in case you are experiencing any of the more rare side affects. A part of the deal of these treatments is that there is, as the saying goes "no free lunches". There will always be a trade off. Tamoxifen has received some bad press over the years; however many millions of women have benefitted from it so far.

One of the best advantages of taking the drug is that it is known to reduce recurrences of breast cancer by approximately 30%. As well it will help to slow down the bone thinning process known as osteoporosis. It is usually recommended that it be taken for no longer than five years. But the problem certainly is complex. In London some years ago, a group of thirty doctors were given one woman's case study in order to suggest treatment regimes for her breast cancer. They came up with over thirty different treatment protocols for this one patient, all seen as valid treatments! So, basically it pays to shop around for the optimum treatment advice. I have had contact with more than one thousand women who have been taking Tamoxifen. With only a couple of exceptions, the feedback has always been good. These women have often found that lifestyle changes including effective stress management are a great combination with this drug. Women who are oestrogen positive also have a positive placebo response associated with the knowledge of the drug's success.

Vaginal discharges are quite common for women taking Tamoxifen, so regular gynaecological checks are recommended, especially when recent research has shown that some people who still have a uterus can develop Tamoxifen-related fibroids or endometrial cancer.

It can be quite confusing trying to sort through information on breast cancer. It seems to depend on which journal one reads as to what the answer might be. But the problem certainly is complex. The case study mentioned earlier is exactly what I mean. So, basically it pays to shop around for the optimum treatment advice.

Chemotherapy

This type of treatment can have obvious short-term side effects, including hair loss, fatigue, nausea and vomiting, as well as reduced immune function, weight gain and menopausal symptoms. Some people even develop arthritis when chemotherapy is discontinued. As you can see from the lengthy list, natural functions as well as a woman's appearance and self-esteem can be compromised.

Again, I am surprised at how many women undergo aggressive treatment regimes without questioning present or future scenarios, without second or third opinions or proper explanation of what to expect in the long term. Again there is often the silence, this passive acceptance.

It appears that people in the UK are relatively new to the idea that they can ask for second opinions and self-help options, particularly in relation to cancer therapies. There has been a social conditioning "that the doctor knows best". This attitude was a product of the old school of medicine. This is now changing with a better qualified, more communicative, more empathetic and a more enquiring generation of doctors. Remember, the doctors want the best results for you too. Be involved, ask questions and don't leave it all to them. I believe very few doctors would be offended if you requested a second, or even a third, opinion. This will be particularly the case if your situation is deemed serious and life altering.

I recently saw a patient who was confronted with permanent and disfiguring facial surgery, after only consulting with one hospital in the south of England. She believed that there had to be other options and she sought other opinions. She received two other opinions that led her to a surgeon in London, who treated her condition successfully, with minimal facial disfigurement.

Drugs are commonly used in various combinations and they may also be used in conjunction with hormonal treatments like Tamoxifen. Ask for a detailed list of your treatment drugs and their possible side effects and take care to make wise decisions.

Hormone Replacement

We need to keep in perspective that our current knowledge on women's hormonal cycles and menopause is still in its embryonic stages. Women, prior to this century, spent most of their years pregnant and breast-feeding, therefore they probably had very little menstrual activity or the experience of menopause at all. Many women died in their early forties in those days.

There is opposing evidence regarding the use of hormone replacement therapy in postmenopausal women. It is now known that ovarian hormones are provided for a woman for her entire life, that the ovaries do not **cease** to function, but rather **change** their function. As already mentioned it is now known that cholesterol can be converted from body fat into estrone, an oestrogen. In fact it is thought that 25% of the positive effects of oestrogen on the cardiovascular system are related to its ability to metabolise cholesterol in a woman's body.

It is now also known that these hormones not only have a localised effect in the body within the organs of reproduction, but are also used systemically. It is now known that oestrogen is involved in four hundred different cellular activities! The more that is discovered about these hormones or messenger molecules, the more we appreciate the body–mind as an incredibly integrated system. For example, due to its positive action on blood vessels, migraine can be relieved by the addition of oestrogen as it can release the constriction in blood flow.

As well as the protective effect on our heart, veins and arteries, oestrogens can also act in the body as free radical scavengers, or as they are commonly known, antioxidants. These substances protect our cells from damage and injury.

Also well known is the positive effect of oestrogen on bone loss and halting osteoporosis, but this will be the subject of our next chapter.

When all of this is considered, it is not surprising that oestrogen deprivation may result in many functional irregularities within women. So it is easy to make a case for Hormone Replacement Therapy (HRT), especially in women who have had an induced early menopause. But still, it is open to conjecture, as some studies state a higher rate of breast cancer among women taking HRT, than those who do not. However, another remarkable and interesting thing was that women who did have breast cancer and who were on HRT had a higher survival rate. It is also worth noting that women who had early menopause have a statistically significant decreased risk of breast cancer. However, if you developed breast cancer premenopause, HRT may carry a risk due to the impact of excess oestrogen so often it is not recommended. Your individual situation needs careful assessment with regular monitoring when dealing with HRT and breast cancer. This is another good reason to have a doctor with whom you can communicate. The usual recommendation is to take the smallest amount that works and you may need professional advice to find an individual dose that works for you.

Oestrogen, when taken on its own (called unopposed oestrogen), caused a problem with cancer of the uterus in women several years ago. Of course this was only of concern to the women who still had their uterus intact. Progesterone was the missing ingredient which caused the lining of the uterus to build up, causing cancer in some women. An artificial progestin is used today in conjunction with oestrogen.

It is a delicate matter of weighing up risks against benefits with your doctor. If it does come to treatment, it is helpful for you to know that there about twenty different combinations of HRT available. Armed with some information, you will be in a better position to discuss the possibilities with your doctor and work out your best course of action. However, I cannot help but wonder about the wisdom we carry within us and how it might be better used. From my experience, women who adopt a regular practice of meditation and stress management do better taking the medical hormonal treatments than those who do not. Because of the positive, balancing effect that meditation can have on our brain chemistry and our hormones, which has been documented, I believe it is the one practice that can safely help women to achieve their own appropriate and individual hormonal balance, in conjunction with their medical treatment.

Suggestions for Managing Menopausal Symptoms

1. Lifestyle changes: Adopting a healthy lifestyle can have a huge impact on menopause management. A nutrient dense diet is essential. Use a diet based on fruits, vegetables and grains. The emphasis should be on including a large amount of fresh vegetables in your diet, especially the leafy greens. A diet that is high in fibre, low in fat, has a low to moderate protein intake and has a low intake of added salt, will increase your wellbeing substantially. Take care not to overload your system with excessive quantities of dairy food. Natural yoghurt, quark, leben and natural cheeses including cottage and ricotta cheeses, are healthy additions to the diet. Low fat content is preferable. That being said some people may need to completely avoid dairy. Check any suspected food sensitivities.
2. Remember, it is not only what you eat but what your body does with what you eat. It has been found that many women over forty show signs of low gastric acid secretion. This means that protein in particular will not be able to be digested properly. There are plenty of natural products, rather than taking more tablets, that cater for

this. For example, horseradish and ginger can be added as a part of your protein meal. I would suggest you ask your health therapist if this is important in your case.

3. If you are having hot flushes, avoid all spicy foods, as they can make the symptoms more unpleasant.

4. Eliminate coffee, lower your alcohol intake to special occasions and deal with your smoking habit if you have one. Be sure not to stop smoking without replacing the habit with, a more health-promoting one — a habit that will be life enhancing. This may mean that a new way of coping with stress in your life may be relevant, especially if you have used smoking as a stress management tool. Think carefully about what smoking means for you. An adequate healthy replacement habit could well be as important as giving up the smoking for health reasons.

5. Check with your doctor that other medications you are taking are not worsening any menopausal symptoms you may have. This can happen easily if you have attended more than one doctor and have not communicated to him or her about the other treatments you are having.

6. For complementary healthcare, do seek the advice of a professional in your chosen modality of treatment. Herbal medicines, homeopathy and other natural therapies will work best when prescribed for your individual needs and situation.

7. Tepid showers can be really helpful for instant management of hot flushes as can a small purse-pack pump-spray containing water. This can also be kept in the refrigerator to make it more refreshing. Try also a drop of pure lavender oil in the spray.

8. On a nutritional basis, supplementation with vitamin E can be very helpful in the control and management of hot flushes. Other helpful supplements can be a multi B group vitamin supplement, antioxidant vitamins and vitamin C with bioflavanoids. These should be prescribed on an individual basis, taking your daily nutritional intake into account.

9. Wear clothing made of natural fibres, thus avoiding promotion of irritation and sweating. Especially wear cotton underwear.
10. Ensure that underwear is not too tight and especially avoid bras that are tight or ill-fitting. A recent American study suggests that tight bras actually may help to develop congestion and irritation of breast tissue. The researchers cross-referenced and compared Western women with cultures who traditionally do not wear breast support!
11. Get plenty of exercise. Brisk walking is very helpful. Exercise has been discovered to help balance oestrogen metabolism and prevent osteoporosis.

"Let your food be your medicine and your medicine be your food." Hippocrates.

Understanding Plant Hormones (Phyto-Oestrogens)

Many plants that are a standard part of our day-to-day diet contain plant oestrogens. On a nutritional basis, for women with breast cancer, plant hormones, in balance with the nutrients that they are partnered with in nature, may be a helpful and unrecognised healing tool in the management of the illness. Foods containing natural substances in balance certainly are preferable to having to take huge quantities of artificial vitamins and minerals. The use of fresh foods including freshly made fruit and vegetable juices, seems to help enormously.

I have noticed, as have various oncologists and other medical people, that patients who are attending to their nutritional needs in this way, often have a corresponding improvement in vitality, general wellbeing and importantly, have fewer complications with treatment side effects. In particular, women dealing with breast cancer seem to obtain exceptional results with their level of wellbeing using these sensible dietary adjustments.

Many of the vegetables commonly recommended for cancer patients are those that are naturally high in plant hormones or phyto-oestrogens. These are present in leafy greens, where high levels of natural calcium also are to be found. More recently the use of soy and soy bi-products has become popular with women who choose to manage hormone problems naturally. There is sound scientific evidence that soy, in a mild way, acts like Tamoxifen. Any women with breast cancer have, therefore, used soy successfully as a part of their treatment. It would be better to be prudent with soy and only incorporate it in your daily diet rather than taking massive supplements of it. As with all plant supplements taking more may not necessarily be better; in fact it can be dangerous in some cases. If you have low oestrogen, plant oestrogen will boost the effects of oestrogen in the body.

Chapter Fifteen

Dealing with the Medical Issues

Breast Cancer: Summary of Four Important Categories

Attention to a woman's emotional life is paramount when dealing with the loss of a breast, invasive and unpleasant treatments, side effects of same, body image, self-esteem, sexuality and other relationships. In my experience, there is a four part scenario that needs attention in the total process of healing.

1. **Pre-diagnosis**: It is interesting to discover how and by what methods women have dealt with their emotional life. The title of the book gives an insight here. The effects of chronic stress and unhappiness with life in general may be key issues needing attention at some time in the healing process. An opportunity is always there to heal your life whether you have a diagnosis of breast cancer or influenza!

2. **At diagnosis time**: Reactions are very varied; however we do know and recognise one important aspect. That is, that women who are diagnosed with breast cancer experience symptoms of post traumatic stress disorder (PTSD). Unfortunately this factor often remains undiagnosed and untreated for many women around the world, and thus it substantially affects their ongoing life quality. For some others diagnosis may be experienced more as relief, linking as it does to feelings that they have felt inside but found no avenue to express. This has been expressed to me many times by women with breast cancer. Even so,

PTSD issues still appear to be applicable at diagnosis in most women.

3. **Post diagnosis and post treatments**: What then? For most women this is a difficult period of adjustment. Because improved treatments are enabling women to live longer with breast cancer the ongoing issue of how to deal with emotions associated with the ever present threat of recurrence remains a challenge. Post treatment *void* can be a fearful time and, as well women are often now dealing with a *life-altering condition* as a consequence of surgery or treatment side effects to which they must adapt on all levels. Also in their memory is the reality that they also have a *life-threatening condition* that could recur. The question of "what if" is one that lives with most women diagnosed with breast cancer. This situation can be a source of ongoing stress that can be alleviated by education about the nature of breast cancer as well as by dealing with the reality of the situation. *Re-empowerment techniques along with other strategies for dealing with setbacks, should they come, are invaluable tools and should be in place early in the breast cancer journey.*

4. **The diagnosis of a recurrence** of breast cancer, particularly if you have followed all the correct advice medically or otherwise can come as a shock. Feelings of vulnerability, disappointment, failure, frustration as well as hopelessness can be experienced. The reality of an uncertain future ensues and life quality can be reduced. Hope and faith can be severely challenged. The more recurrences there are, the harder it can be to bounce back, to keep your focus and your energy. Rather than being viewed as a negative issue or as a failure of treatments, women can be shown how to reframe their situation if they are armed with the ammunition of prior knowledge and educated as to the behaviour of breast cancer. The development of resilience has been demonstrated as a significant tool as patients face the challenge of their illness. The issue of living well despite active disease is a part of their ability to flourish in the presence of adversity.

Here we are speaking of the important issue of quality of life, not curing of illness. I have known many clients who have lived well with active cancer for more than twenty years and remained quite resilient to the effects; not because of denial but because of the way they have chosen to respond to the challenge of the illness. There is a need to put the fear of a recurrence into perspective. I have also known people who were resilient and apparently healthy who were suddenly confronted by uninvited life-change. Their pre-learned quality helped them to adjust, heal and adapt to the new but un-chosen life and live with life-altering conditions. You see, just because you practise a healthy lifestyle, does not mean you are immune to life and to all it brings; but it may mean that when major life-changes occur, you have more reserve and resilience to deal with it.

Robert Louis Stevenson wrote: *"Life is like a card game, it is not about being dealt a good hand; but playing a bad hand well."*

Prevention of Breast Cancer and Promotion of Breast Health

Prevention of disease and promotion of breast health is long overdue. As the reader, I hope that you will find great benefit from the information that addresses the physical, psychological, emotional and spiritual aspects of illness. It is now known and recognised that many cancers are preventable and yes, you can contribute positively by choosing and enacting simple lifestyle changes. But realistically that is not the whole story. Life and healing is a mystery. We don't have all the answers … we just do the best we can.

Diagnosis Time

Diagnosis time can invoke many different responses. For some it may come as a relief as well as a shock. The manner in which women are told both their diagnosis and their prognosis, can make an enormous difference to the overall management of the illness, as well as the outcome. With a diagnosis of cancer, the doctor can clearly set an atmosphere that will enable the patient to respond either with an attitude of challenge and a view to possible healing, or to give in to the perceived power and fear of cancer. This is a point where a doctor really does hold the power of life and death in his or her hands.

Breast cancer so often is represented in a way that instills and breeds fear into the minds and hearts of women. Fortunately today many breast cancers are detected sooner than they were in the past. For the amount of information that the medical profession knows about cancer there is an equal amount that they still don't know. One thing that we do know is, that despite billions of dollars being poured into research, the medical management of cancer is still a fledgling in finding the cure and cancer rates are still rising. We know that people have spontaneous remissions and that self-help methods can activate and play a part in those remissions. We know that your psychological state, belief systems and ability "to think outside the square" all help in your recovery. With breast cancer we also know that there is likely to be some sort of alteration to our female body; an intrusion whose scars go way beneath the surface of the outer skin. The depth of this intrusion may not be understood by a medical practitioner whose whole life is focused on the technical details of getting it right for his or her patients. Importantly, you do need a good technician; but don't expect them to be all things to all people. Hopefully they will refer you to areas of the hospital or outside sources you for the extra emotional support that you need.

If you are diagnosed by a medical profession that believes your cancer has no known cause and no known guarantee of cure you can see the predicament that many oncologists find themselves in. For you as the patient, there is perhaps some prior knowledge that may cause you to fear any disfiguring and aggressive treatments that are recommended and that are viewed purely as palliative. Living in a society whose basic belief system supports that view, the picture may not seem all that rosy! The promotion of "cancer" as a word and not a "sentence" sounds good in theory, but when it comes to a woman's turn to be a patient this slogan is well gone to the background. Most people still have fears of cancer, so my patients tell me.

One area where it seems that oncologists could improve, is in the area of communication skills at diagnosis time. Careful choice of words at a time when a patient is the most vulnerable, is more than warranted. Whether or not the doctor's choice of words are positively or negatively perceived by the patient, can be seen to be setting the tone for the entire time of the patient's cancer experience. I think that many oncologists may forget this unless it is brought to their attention by an empowered patient. It is also fair to say that what is heard by the patient may not be what the oncologist has said. This is not uncommon at the time of initial diagnosis when patients are informed of their medical conditions and treatments. All information can be lost in an abyss of shock, confusion and bewilderment. How interesting it is, that for these people, somewhere deep within them there is a listening ear that hears the word cancer, hears the word prognosis and then becomes deaf to any other information given.

If the patient has a negative view of the cancer word then the very mention of the name as applied to them can initiate a response in the brain known as a *scatoma*. This is a term used for the walling off to information mechanism that threatens survival.

The following story illustrates one important aspect of communication concerning a breast cancer patient's body image and self-esteem. Rhonda was an attractive woman in her mid-thirties who was diagnosed with a large but early stage breast cancer that necessitated a partial mastectomy. Her oncologist was giving her information about the procedure, trying to ignore the tears that were obviously welling up in her eyes. His words were meant to be informative and kind, informing her that she had options about the future shape of her breast. However his choice of words, rather than the information, had left her in a highly distressed state. He had told her that obviously the operation would leave her with a deformed and misshapen breast; but not to worry as she could have an implant to hide the ugliness! Rhonda had already made up her mind that if the diagnosis was cancer and she had to lose a breast, she would accept it and would not have an implant. The mention of the descriptive words ugly, misshapen and deformed were worse for Rhonda to deal with than the surgery itself. Breast cancer is such a very complex field of emotional material!

While some people have a natural positivity that carries them through difficult circumstances, many of the people I work with have needed to *learn* how to develop a more positive state of mind. They have succeeded in this and transformed their lives.

What people who are feeling hopeless and helpless in the face of life-threatening illness need to hear, are words that can heal. Words that can engender hope. This is not false hope; but a suggestion of open-ended possibilities. Patients need to be in an atmosphere conducive to the encouragement of faith.

While it is quite possible to create this atmosphere in a caring medical setting, many patients complain of being affected by an overwhelming sense of medical doom and gloom. To be given a sentence or prognosis that involves the patient taking on a specific time limit for their life, almost always leads to a punctual appointment with death. If a patient takes this prognosis to a deep level within, I often feel powerless to help them to survive. Often, these people have lost their spirit, their will to live. Their belief system cannot accommodate possibility thinking or the will to heal. Instead of offering hope a negative prognosis can give a message from which they may not recover. This message is very difficult to overwrite and often the best that one can offer in this scenario is the possibility of a good death. A patient can take on a definite prognosis like a negative affirmation. This becomes imprinted and therefore becomes part of the belief of the person. Hypnosis can be the solution for patients who have been given a negative or poor prognosis. Under hypnosis the prognosis can be re-framed into an open-ended outcome. That is to say that possibility becomes one of the choices.

Maybe prognosis time could be an appropriate moment to access any skills of denial or ignorance that you have acquired!

The following series of short, true stories, will give you an understanding of how this works in practice. Our first story is an incredible one, demonstrating the healing abilities of the mind–body connection and the power of a patient's belief system.

An American "hill-billy" was diagnosed with throat cancer by his general practitioner. He told him that he would have to go to a large city hospital in order to have the cancer treated. The doctor also told him that this hospital had a new form of ray treatment that would cure his cancer.

The man was awed by the large hospital and after arrival there, was given a basic check up. When a thermometer was placed in this naïve man's mouth, his doctor realised that the man thought that it was his ray treatment! After several sessions of this "wonder treatment" the man was cured — his cancer disappeared completely!

The next two stories powerfully demonstrate how belief systems can either turn on or turn off the *will to live*. These were both recorded by medical physiologist Walton Cannon. From his diary he states:

Dr S. M. Lambert of the Western Pacific Health Service of the Rockefeller Foundation wrote to me on several occasions as he had seen evidence of death from fear. In one case there was a startling recovery. At a mission at Mona Mona in North Queensland, were many native converts, but on the outskirts of the mission was a group of non-converts, including one "Nebo", a famous witch doctor. The chief helper of the missionary was Rob, a native who had been converted. When Dr Lambert arrived at the Mission he learned that Rob was in distress and that the missionary wanted him examined. Dr Lambert made the examination, and found no fever, no complaint of pain, no symptoms or signs of disease. He was impressed, however, by the obvious indications that Rob was seriously ill and extremely weak. From the missionary he learned that Rob had had a bone pointed at him by Nebo and was convinced that, in consequence, he must die. Thereupon, Dr Lambert and the missionary went for Nebo, threatened him sharply that his supply of food would be shut off if anything happened to Rob and that he and his people would be driven away from the mission. At once Nebo agreed to go with them to see Rob. He leaned over Rob's bed and told the sick man that it was all a mistake, a mere joke — indeed, that he had not pointed a bone at all.

The relief, Dr Lambert testifies, was almost instantaneous. That evening Rob was back at work, quite happy again and in full possession of his physical strength.

A less fortunate outcome is reported in the next account. Dr Lambert wrote to me concerning an experience of Dr P. S. Clarke with Kanakas working on the sugar plantations of North Queensland.

One day a Kanaka came to his hospital and told him he would die in a few days because a spell had been put upon him and nothing could be done to counteract it. The man who had been known to Dr Clarke for some time was given a very thorough examination, including an examination of the stool and urine. All was found normal, but as he lay in bed he gradually grew weaker. Dr Clarke called upon the foreman of the Kanakas to come to the hospital to give the man assurance, but on reaching the foot of the bed, the foreman leaned over, looked at the patient, and then turned to Dr Clarke, saying, "Yes, doctor, close up him he die." (that is he is nearly dead). The next day, at 11 o'clock in the morning, he ceased to live.

Compare the technique used in the last two stories with our hill-billy friend from the first story. The first story gives a positive message to the patient, of hope of a cure. He is then given a treatment with a technique and a ritual by which the cure can happen (i.e. the use of the thermometer). He believes that this treatment will cure him. Whereas in our other two stories, the belief systems of the tribe dictate the outcome.

The belief system decrees that if you are "pointed" with a bone by the witch doctor, then without exception you will die. With hope removed and a strong belief and expectation that death will be the result, the mind–spirit connection of the patient seals the decree and so the death completes a self-fulfilling prophecy.

Bone Pointing or the Negative Placebo: The Story That Does Not Heal

Just as someone can create a story with images of a life-affirming nature, so they can create one that has a negative impact upon the will to live. According to our belief system both of these powerful affirmations can enter our consciousness and direct the spirit or soul nature to extinguish the spark of life — the will to live. Such is the nature of *bone pointing* or the negative placebo response, as it is known in the therapeutic world. I have personally witnessed this power of belief, as related to healing, in many other cultures throughout the world, as well as in the context of orthodox medical practice.

In my mother country, Australia, our indigenous aboriginal society has a code of ethical conduct, which, if transgressed in a serious manner, may result in one being "pointed". The "pointing" is ceremoniously cast upon the transgressor of the tribal law, by a medicine man or *Kadaitja* man as he is known in Central Australia. A human femur bone, decorated sometimes with clay and feathers is the instrument of power that is pointed at the person. The medicine man is a man of high degree, capable of strong thought powers. The person who is pointed knows that once this has happened, he is as good as dead. He is then shunned by all and will not be able to cope, becoming hopeless and helpless. There can be no hope or expectation of help from any outside source. With his social structure destroyed, he waits for death. Just prior to death, the tribe gathers to say good-bye and he dies.

The cancer story, I believe, is a more modern-day ritual, similar in many ways to bone pointing. In cancer, belief systems and strong thoughts about disease have the power to be life-giving or destroying. The difference being, that somehow in Western society, we have forgotten about the power of healing through using a patient's own belief system as well as ritual.

For the medical profession it is now a matter of choosing how to tell the story to the patient even when the outcome is not, in their view, expected to be one of curing. For the patient, it is a matter of choice whether they wish to accept a poor prognosis or not. There is an obvious need for honesty, clarity and directness at diagnosis time, but not for the sacrifice of the subtle but important life qualities like hope, faith, and love. There are things in our lives that we cannot quantify through science. Things that make the living-ness of life throb with the passion to be. If medicine fails to provide sustenance to feed the will to survive and encourage the will to heal, it is lacking in one of the most crucial elements in healing. Spirit, thought and belief needs to take their rightful position again in medicine. Currently medicine has an emphasis on treating, cure and palliation rather than healing. Healing, in fact, is a very important part of palliative care and of the delivery of care in the hospice situation. Here the task is to help people to die well, which incorporates the unloading of unfinished business, or healing. Each has its part to play in caring for the patient, but it is the fusion of the two that will lead to a better way of living and a medicine that serves its people.

How Women React Emotionally to Diagnosis

A difficult time for patients and their partners around the time of diagnosis is usual. This is an experience that no-one can prepare either of you for. The best that everyone can do, however, is to be honest with feelings and emotions. Often, great understanding and compassion is required as there may be unfamiliar emotions demonstrated, especially in the company of family and friends. For, while a patient may appear passive with medical helpers, some women will rediscover their feelings with great intensity, discharging them in the safety of the home environment. Mood swings can be of some concern, but it is far better to allow yourself the luxury to really feel how you feel, for maybe even a week or two. Some women can move through and express moods of grief, shock, denial, anger, or resentment, and may even find themselves bargaining for time with God in their private prayer moments. These reactions to diagnosis are stages of grief that are quite similar to the stages of dying that Dr Elisabeth Kubler-Ross talks about in her classic *Death and Dying*. They are also normal responses and can be re-framed as the dying off of the old to allow the creation of the new.

For some, the symptoms post diagnosis can be more protracted. Some women will cope well enough on their own, while others will benefit from outside help. It can be quite an individual experience that depends upon many factors.

Taking this individuality into consideration is so important in helping the patient find what is best for them to do. For example I could see six patients in the one day who have the same type of breast cancer, but they will all need a different approach from me because of their individuality. By understanding their individuality and listening to their story it is easier to find out more about who they are and how they perceive the world. There is usually information that is hidden much deeper than their symptoms present. Del's and Betty's stories highlight just how different people can be in coping with their breast cancer diagnosis.

Del's Story

I remember Del as a woman who reacted and coped in a unique way to her diagnosis. Best described as a rather crusty woman, she had been brought up in the Australian bush where her dad had practised as a general practitioner. With her dry wit and a steely exterior, she had the appearance of a woman who had just stepped out of a Crocodile Dundee movie set! I really enjoyed her humour and her earthiness and enjoyed visiting her at home.

She had, as she expressed it, "taken a lot of knocks in her life" and she was indeed a strong and independent woman, a loner who had kept to herself. Apart from her two old dogs and a small herd of milking goats, she lived alone. She really loved her old dogs. She introduced them to me like human members of her family when I paid a visit to her home. They were introduced as the world's best counsellors, because they said nothing, gave her their attention, were good listeners and gave lots of love! I took that comment as a strong hint!

She had been diagnosed with breast cancer and saw no difficulty with the idea of a mastectomy. "Well", she said dryly, "what do I need them for, I'm past the "change" and there's no blokes in my life to have to worry about all that. I told the doctor to just get rid of the damn thing (the breast). Can't let a little thing like that interfere with my life can I?" I was unusually lost for words!

Del had recovered quickly from her surgery and refused any further treatment as she said she had a total belief that the surgery would be successful. Her father had always told her that the best thing to do with breast cancer was to remove the breast. She told me that her dad was a great believer in surgery and she had seen the results of his many "miracle" patients.

This cancer was not going to slow her down. After all, she had just bought herself a new chainsaw before diagnosis, and she was keen try it out! "You know, I reckon I've just let myself get a bit down over things. My brother Jack died last year, the last of my relatives. Knocked me a bit, it did. I guess I've just got to get on with life, I'm not ready to meet my maker yet!"

Del fully believed that ridding herself of her diseased breast would fully cure her. It did. She lived on for another twenty years in good health and died from a heart attack due to over-exertion. In all the time I knew Del, I never once offered her advice. I would simply sit and have a cup of tea, buy my goats' milk, listen and leave. Although her exterior was weathered and wrinkled from long exposure to the hot Australian sun, Del had a heart of gold and a pioneering feminine strength that I can instantly recall to this day. Definitely not the chiffon type of femininity, but Del was a survivor whose demeanor reflected the authentic magic of the wise woman. I learned much from her.

Betty's Story

Betty, on the other hand, was a lady in the true sense of the word. Unlike Del, she had been very particular and proud of her appearance, and always presented herself in a manner that highlighted her attractiveness. A perfectionist by nature, the effect of the removal of one breast was devastating to her and sent the whole structure of her life into chaos. After diagnosis and without being given the time to comprehend or psychologically adapt to life with one breast, Betty was scheduled for surgery within days. Her doctor said that this was due to a "fortunate" cancellation. Clearly not coping, she underwent a mastectomy. She had no time to think or plan her life and she had been given no advice about any type of breast reconstruction nor was she offered any counselling services. Betty had quite large breasts and the lack of one of them not only caused physical problems for her in terms of balance but also she experienced tremendous difficulties with self-esteem and appearance. After the surgery, both Betty and her husband suffered from the effects of shock that had resulted from the trauma. Neither of them were good communicators so their way of responding was just to wall themselves off from everyone including the medical staff.

Sadly, but not surprisingly, Betty suffered post-surgical depression — and I mean suffered, in the true sense of the word. Eventually shock therapy was recommended as the treatment of choice, and for a while it did snap her out of her depressed state. This helped Betty to be functional on a day-to-day basis and her inner self retreated more and more. I saw Betty and her husband only when she had been diagnosed with bone secondaries. It had been her husband's decision to come and see me. He had decided to talk. I was shocked to see a woman whose outer presence was quite strong, but whose inner life was clearly clouded behind distant and disconnected eyes. I knew of the shaman practice of re-connecting a patient's essence or soul force. The healing for this condition was called soul retrieval. Soul loss conveyed an accurate image that portrayed just how much of this woman's spirit was missing.

It took about half an hour into the conversation before I felt any reconnection with Betty at all. Her passive and emotionless exterior masked the fierceness of her pain. But with wise counsel, that is, me encouraging her to talk, whilst I listened attentively, she slowly began to become animated. There we were, one speaker and one listener soul to soul. During that consultation Betty had made a major decision to rekindle the spark of life and retrieve, piece by piece, the missing links. Unlike Del, who was glad to see the tail end of her breast, it was not so for Betty. Such is the uniqueness of each person's journey.

As the story unfolded, Betty had not ever been able to grieve for her missing breast, and she confided in me that she had been unable to look at her body in a mirror since the surgery. Rather than taking showers, she would take bubble baths that would hide the disfigurement (*her words*) from view. In conversation she often referred to her mastectomy site as "the scene of the crime". Her husband was an incredibly dedicated and committed man who supported Betty through the most terrible times, and never gave up hope of retrieving his wife back from a void that he could neither see nor understand. Unlike Rhonda in our earlier story, Betty would have responded more positively if she *had* been offered a breast implant. Although it was many years on and she was dealing with bone secondaries, she found a compassionate surgeon who agreed to reconstruct her breast. This was a woman who could not live a normal life without a breast. Such is the individuality of breast cancer diagnosis and treatments.

How Can Cancer Services be Improved?

The following was obtained by surveying patients of several cancer support groups. They were asked from their point of view how the delivery of services could be improved.

The Patients' View: Where does the medical system provide ineffective management?

Technical Skills:

- Delayed diagnosis, ineffective diagnosis.
- Poor clinical judgment.
- Dismissing reported symptoms.
- Over-familiarity, becoming too casual with symptoms/patient.
- Poorly matched referrals (in personal sense).
- An inability to communicate treatments and procedures at a patient's level of understanding.

Communication Skills:

- Removing hope, "pointing of the bone!"
- Lack of time.
- Poor communication generally.
- Holier than thou attitude:
    — intellectual superiority.
    — non-disclosure of information.
    — resentment of questioning. Get angry when asked about options.
    — professional or personal ego problems.
- "Difficult patient" syndrome.

Attitudes:

- Closed mind — barrier to the non-scientific approaches.

- Tunnel vision — the impact of specialisation.
- Treat the disease and overlook, or avoid, the person.
- Lack of knowledge and/or acceptance of self-help techniques.
- Dismiss as "alternative nonsense" the right to have choice — including natural and complementary therapies.

What patients would like from their doctors:

We want ACCESS to:

- The best available medical treatment.
- The best available self-help techniques.

We would like you:

- To be good communicators.
- Provide information — the truth underpinned with hope.
  - Be careful with use of statistics.
  - To advise on all options.
  - To advise on lifestyle issues after first treatment.
  - To help us avoid recurrences.
  - Use language I can understand.
  - Answer questions.
- Be positive, understand our situation.
- Use listening skills.
- Give time when it's really needed — be available:
  - for appointments (as long as it is arranged).
  - after hours — emergency.
  - for reassurance!
- Treat me as a person, not just a disease.
- Provide ongoing support regardless of my choices.
- Be a partner in my healing. Be someone I can trust.

Patients' suggestions to improve communication:

- Understand that I may not be acting normally.
- Sit close to me and avoid barriers (e.g. desks).
- Please touch me.
- Shake my hand.
- Hug, if congruent.

- Make eye contact.
- Listen to me.
- Acknowledge what you hear.
- Seek confirmation that your messages are heard.
- Use educational aids including handouts.
- Reinforce what you say frequently.
- Recommend that partners attend consultations.
- Advise that we take notes or tape major consultations.
- Respect my feelings, beliefs and hopes.
- Take an interest in my family.

Don't deny yourself treatment with the best that medical technology can give us. Both patients and doctors still have much to learn in the field of breast cancer. Let's keep communicating, providing the feedback and applying as much self-help for our situation as we can. You may see yourself as a long-term survivor of cancer, but due to the constant exposure to statistics and mortality rates, your doctor may not. You need to get him or her on side or at least to give some approval and support for your choices. It is helpful if your doctor endorses your choice to use and choose other therapies to enhance your medical treatments. Communication needs to be on both sides.

It has often been said of my ex-husband, that statistically he should be dead, but he is alive all these years later. I have met thousands of people around the world who have had cancer and survived, despite being given poor prognoses. These people have accessed and used an enormous variety of therapies and self-help methods that *they found they could believe in*. Just as there are as many reasons for getting cancer as grains of sand on the beach it is likely that the cure or healing of cancer will also be multi-factorial. Make a healing plan that graduates in stages rather than changing everything at once. Be careful not to feel overwhelmed by thinking that you have to do it all at once. Healing and curing is a process. It can take many years and so as you take your journey remind yourself of **The Three Stages of Healing** and above all always be gentle with yourself.

Chapter Sixteen

The Importance of Cancer Support Groups

My work and experience with cancer support groups has its origins in direct experience rather than from studies and research programmes that have been set up to study the outcomes. This has possibly made a difference to my views about support groups that are formed away from the usual oncology and hospital departments. Many people have presumed that a support group will be a threatening experience and that there would be no way that people would open up in a group of strangers. However this proves to be unfounded in practice. Once the initial bonding has taken place there is an immediate ease that develops in relating not only the story of a person's cancer but also the story of their life. This is a process that actually has to be experienced to be understood. Feedback from our patients and carers has indicated that support group participants would rather have their support group outside of the hospital environment, where they have often experienced treatments or tests that they would rather forget about. Perhaps an initial activity for patients is to be informed about or to attend a hospital group in the early stages and then be referred to local groups.

There are many types of cancer support groups and it is useful to know this so that you can attend the group most appropriate for your needs.

Support groups can be:

- Non-structured and just nice social occasions. They work well for networking and support and to find a listening ear and expression.
- Those that serve an educative purpose, providing information on local resources and a get together for women with similar experiences. Support and understanding are important as well.
- Structured with a set programme for each week and conducted by an experienced leader who may be a past patient or carer.
- Structured as a therapeutic group led by a psychologist, psychotherapist or psychiatrist. Nurses may conduct some cancer support groups.
- Groups such as the breast cancer support programmes (H.O.P.E. groups) that I have founded, have a six-week cycle. Patients and the group leader discuss a different topic each week and, for half of the time, practise some form of stress management. It is important that everyone also gets the time to tell their story so the first session of the six weeks would be a one day session where people bond and get to know each other and build trust in the group process and the group leader. In this type of group, issues of the body, mind, emotion and spirit would be addressed. After the six weeks, this group can go on to another group for a further six week advanced programme or they can choose to meet informally and keep the connections and networks alive. Many lasting friendships form from these groups due to the intimacy of knowing the other at a very personal level.

The success of a support group will very much depend on the skills and empathy of the leader. The more therapeutic work involved, the greater the skill required to manage the group. There can be quite a deal of emotional material and baggage uncovered at these groups and the leader needs to be both skilled enough to manage and yet not take any of this personally on board. Therefore current or ex-patients who start their own groups beware and be conscious of really focusing on your own self-care. Without the knowledge of how to keep your boundaries in place an unwary leader can find that their own health can become compromised as a result.

A group with small numbers of eight to ten people will generally be more intense and therapeutic. However a small group can have particular issues especially if some of the participants are quite ill. The group leader needs the experience to manage and troubleshoot issues for the group should two or three members die. This can be an immediate issue for an ongoing group with small numbers, if the members keep meeting afterwards.

Groups of twelve to sixteen members however, can manage the grief from the loss of two or three group members better, due to the size of the group. Larger groups take a good deal of skill to lead, but the interaction, networking and connection make it worthwhile.

Participants

Cancer support groups can be what is termed open or closed; this means with a changing or fixed attendance. A changing group of participants does not have the same level of trust and bonding that a fixed group of attendees will. If partners, husbands or lovers attend with the patients I have found a strong inhibition to talk about the real issues. The conversation tends towards superficiality under these circumstances. The beauty of being with people whom you don't know means that they have no fixed ideas about who you are and it also means that there can be no unspoken emotional baggage between couples. The latter can really affect expression of the truth and the real issues. I prefer to have separate groups for friends or carers and see them privately or have one-day workshops for them.

I also prefer to have a mixed group of patients, from those newly diagnosed to those who have had or still have secondaries. This type of structure really needs a lot of skill so that the early diagnosed patients do not go home terrified from the stories of the more seasoned patients. In fact when well managed, there can be a great deal of helpful material that the seasoned patients can share with the more recently diagnosed. It can also result in encouraging the reality of the situation to be opened up for discussion.

Ongoing Support

When you choose your support group make sure that there will be some kind of follow-on or contact available for you. Newsletters, reunions, network groups, phone or email contacts are useful. It is important that they are able to be accessed either regularly or when needed. In your group you will learn many new skills and methods and you may be opened up to new ideas about yourself and the world. It is important that you can have the ongoing support in case you have a setback of some kind. An "umbilical cord" or lifeline to a group or organisation can be helpful in times of questioning or crisis.

What Can You Expect from a Support Group

Research tells us that by attending a cancer support group you can:

- Extend your life. Some studies have found that women with advanced secondary cancer who attended a cancer support group could double their life expectancy.

We also know that if you attend an educative type of group:

- Your quality of life will improve.
- Your ability to share and connect with others will improve.
- You will have the opportunity to find meaning in your life.
- You can reconnect with your passion, your *joie de vivre*.

- You may learn to use the illness to reframe and heal past trauma.
- You will learn day-to-day techniques for effective stress management.
- You will have an opportunity to tell your life story as well as the story of your cancer; a very healing process.

Remember to ask for help. Many women have been through the experience of breast cancer and many will come after you. You are not alone. Ask about support groups or explore them on the internet. Support groups help the healing.

Chapter Seventeen

Carers

Carers Who Want to be Involved in Your Healing Programme

Some Pointers for the Patient

You are one of the fortunate patients if you have a husband, partner or close supporter who wants to know what you are doing, what your goals are and wants to help you achieve them. There are many kinds of carers and their methods of showing care, or proactively demonstrating it, are very different.

Some prime carers, due to financial or employment circumstances, can only lend supporting spirit; while others can make the time to be more involved. Most patients prefer to have a carer who displays some level of activity especially in helping with the practical day-to-day chores. For women, it is important to remember that men will often show their care by *doing* things for you whereas you might be looking for concern, sympathy, a listening ear, touch and intimacy. I have seen this issue create major problems between couples which have been the final straw that has destroyed the marriage or relationship.

If healthy communication has been lacking throughout your relationship, it will be highlighted now more than ever before. If you are involved in healing as a couple, I would suggest that you prioritise your attention towards learning how to communicate more effectively with one another. Being silent about the change in family dynamics that a life-threatening illness brings, will only make it more difficult as time goes by. You will need to establish new roles and responsibilities and, if there are children involved, organizational details about care and after school activities will need to be addressed. As the patient you will need, of necessity, to take time out for self-care.

Do not, however, expect husbands to do things that they are just not capable of doing. This advice can save you much time, anguish and frustration. It is far better that you use your cancer support network, counsellor, clergyman or best friend to discuss some of the more important intimate and personal issues around your breast cancer. It is vital that you fully apply your healing intelligence towards how you organise your support system right at the outset. This is an essential part of the post diagnosis process that you go through and, in particular, it becomes the cornerstone in ensuring the success of everything you do, whether it is surgery, treatment, complementary or alternative care. Without the support structures in place, your healing programme can turn into a stressful nightmare. Learn to plan and use every resource that you can and read and learn about self-help techniques that suit your particular situation.

Why Husbands, Carers, Partners Back Off

There are many reasons and the more common ones are listed below:

- You don't include or inform them. Are you a *Woman of Silence*?
- They do not want to be informed or included. Are they silent too?
- They don't understand about breast cancer. They should attend a doctor's appointment with you, ask questions and be clear about what you are dealing with. Not just the fact that it is breast cancer but, further, understanding more about the severity of the illness can provide them with a framework for planning how they will manage it. Depending on the circumstances, a prognosis can be unhelpful. For example, if a carer knows that a prognosis

is say, twelve months, then it radically affects their intention to be able to effectively help the patient.

- They are fearful about your outcome. Husbands and partners who have previously cared for and lost mothers to breast cancer or other serious illness, are often coloured in their thinking about cancer. There may be quite valid reasons why they can't cope.
- Maybe your relationship has not been healthy for a long time and your illness then becomes the trigger for them to remove themselves either physically or emotionally or both.
- They may feel that you are leaning on them too heavily and not taking enough responsibility for your own situation.
- There is a chance that you might be burdening an already overloaded partner with extra duties. By accessing local community and volunteer services, you can go shopping with relative ease and be taken to the necessary appointments.
- Beware of the issue of conditional support, often used as a lever by both. It is one thing to have boundaries, but conditional support gets into the area fraught with danger when partners bargain with each other for favours and love. Where there is conditional support on either side, there is no love.
- Avoid comparing them to other partners. Making them feel guilty will not help your cause.
- They often feel that they and the family may have to make too many changes, including lifestyle changes, which they are unable or unprepared to make.
- Are you communicating your needs clearly enough? Just because you voice your needs does not mean, however, that they will be met. How well they are met will tell you something about the state of your relationship. If they are not, you need to determine how you can deal with that level of disappointment.
- They may have genuine concerns about losing their employment if they take time off to support you. This is a real issue for single income families.

- If you need to talk about death, either the real possibility of it or a fear about what your future might hold, then the person to speak with is, must be, your partner. Some patients choose to exclude them, falsely believing that they are protecting them. After death, the carers are the ones left behind and it makes such a difference to their life quality, and their ability to move on, if you can openly discuss issues around death. Unfinished business usually affects carers for some time.
- Remember, as the patient, it is your illness; but it has also radically changed the lives of your partner and your family. Be understanding!
- As a general rule, the longer a relationship has endured pre-diagnosis, the more likely it is that it will endure the trauma of your illness. Deep bonding that comes with the years tends to be strong emotional glue when things are tough!

Complementary and Alternative Medicine and the Partner/Carer

You need to keep your healing programme simple and try and introduce changes gradually. Some regimes that purport cures using alternative medicine, stringent dietary regimes, megavitamin supplements and lots of fresh juices, can really put pressure on a relationship. Emotionally, these approaches can make you and your partner even more vulnerable and more stressed. Often the stress of trying to implement and pay for this is a very real issue for many households. For this to work, you really need a partner who understands what you are trying to do. It is not that these approaches don't work, but it is often better if they are incorporated into your programme when you feel empowered, present and more in control of your own life. What is unpleasant to hear from either dying people or bereaved partners are statements like: "If only we had done the diet better or meditated more, then maybe it would be different". If this was the desired outcome of alternative medicine, to make people feel failures in death or bereavement, then I would hang up my healer's hat!

We tend to make better choices, more conscious choices, if we are in charge of our lives. Believing in what you do as a patient is crucial if your partner is involved too. Your belief system activates your healing system. Intention, as well as attention, to your goals is important for the both of you.

I am speaking here from direct and personal experience. I was the partner who totally devoted my life to a juicing machine, supplements and enemas for eighteen hours each day for many months. It was demanding and exhausting work. Experience, and obtaining formal qualifications since, has taught me that things psychological, emotional and spiritual are the most important things to attend to first and foremost. When, and if, you die as a result of the illness, or when you die eventually as we all have to, I don't think it will be important how many carrot juices you ingested. Rather it is the quality of your relationships with others and your relationship with yourself, including dealing with unfinished business, which will be most important.

If you or your partner wishes to embark upon, or have already begun, a stringent regime, then make sure that you are enjoying it. Ensure that it is not a stress that creates a wedge between the two of you. The power of two can be a phenomenal power if used positively. At the moment I have two tomato plants in my kitchen. Everything about their handling has been identical except that as they have grown larger I have only staked and supported one of them. The supported one is doing so much better than the unsupported.

This reminds me of an African story:

A very old man in a village knows that he is nearing his time of death. He calls together his children to tell them and prepare them for his imminent passing. He reached for the earth, picked up one stick and snapped it. "See how easily it breaks," he said. Then he picked up two identical sticks. He held them together and tried to

break them; they did not break. "See," he said," the combined
strength of each other will see you through!"

Support or No Support: Is That the Question?

Having a live-in, supporting partner has many advantages, especially in terms of the practical issues of life; however, some patients arrange things differently to suit their own situation. Sometimes taking the journey of breast cancer on your own can have advantages. Those to whom I have spoken, whether they are single, divorced or separated, all say there are some advantages in going it alone. Some of their comments are listed below:

- You have no-one else to answer to.
- You can do what you like, when you like.
- You don't have to prove to someone else the worth of what you are doing, particularly in order to get their support.
- You can be in charge of your own situation.

Experiences of Being a Carer

Being a partner of a person who develops a life-threatening illness is an incredibly challenging place to be. When I was in this situation at the age of twenty-two, I found that being a carer was one of the loneliest vocations in the world. It was made even lonelier by the fact that he had a shocking prognosis and because I wanted to try to help him. His medical practitioners, friends and family saw me as a dreamer who had unrealistic goals. However, when he recovered three years later, there was silence! Some said he was just lucky, but for the most part, those very same people who were critical of the possibility of his recovery, ignored its reality. As the carer who took most of the brunt of choices that we had made, I began to feel almost invisible. However, as a result of the number of different things that we did, many practitioners, who only had a brief role in the healing process, seemed to want to own the outcome; yet they had abandoned us when things were not going well! Suffice to say, that as a proactive carer, you will have your mettle, patience, and commitment well and truly tested. But the real gift is in selfless giving if you can manage it, but it is not easy. Usually we do things because there may be a spin-off for us. In this case, there may be little recognition or even appreciation from anyone. However, as a human being, there is usually a deep spiritual contentment that comes from the process of "right action" towards another being. If you consciously make the choice to be a carer, for someone with breast cancer, you will have no regrets; whatever the outcome. After all, the best that one can only ever give, is one's best.

Some Pointers for the Carer

- Decide what your role will be as early as possible and make plans about how you will achieve your goal. Let your partner know how you are feeling.
- Don't play games; don't pretend all is well when it is not.
- Communicate and write things down that have been decided.
- If there are children involved, decide how, when and what you will tell them; be consistent in your dealings with them.
- Review your situation in relation to your partner, and the family, regularly.
- Keep your boundaries intact. As much as you love someone, it is important that you recognise their need for personal space and that they recognise yours.
- Find someone that you can share and talk with regularly. Don't be a loner or a martyr.
- Realise that this is your partner's illness. Your journey as carer will be different. The image I have for this is two intersecting circles.
- Remember that patients can sometimes seem self-centred or even selfish. Understand what it might be like for them.

- Use resources well; especially those small tasks that can be done by other people on your behalf.
- Find a hobby or pastime, if you don't already have one, to help ease the tensions and provide some relaxation and fun.
- If you sense your relationship is in difficulty don't ignore it. It won't go away. Even after someone has died, unfinished business can linger on which will still affect you for many years to come.
- If death is imminent, talk about it. If you can't manage it, find someone who can give you help and spiritual direction. Read about it.
- Be honest with yourself, your family and your partner.

Children and Breast Cancer

When there are children involved in the family dynamic of breast cancer, there are some special requirements. Children are very honest within themselves. From my experience with younger children such as leukaemia patients, they seem to have an incredible wisdom and connection with life and death. They draw pictures of angels and talk candidly about their death and about their family. I have learned much from these wise and courageous little souls. In the case of a mother with breast cancer, and depending upon their ages, children basically do very well with a simple explanation. They also do well if we are honest with them. If they see mummy sick they need to know why, as this alleviates a tremendous amount of anxiety and worry for them. If they know that you are talking with them and will tell them what is going on they are often okay about it. One issue that I have commonly experienced is from well meaning staff at schools where, without knowing the real situation, they will often be overly sympathetic. Children will then suspect that something is really wrong. The peer group can be supportive to children at certain ages but it can also create difficulties, as evidenced by the experience of the patient in the following example.

215

Margaret had tried unsuccessfully for years to have children. As a last resort she enlisted in the IVF programme where she was given high doses of oestrogen; still she failed to become pregnant. Her husband, Martin, suggested that they should apply for adoption before they were too old and, as usually happens with a highly suitable couple, they were soon to adopt a Korean daughter, followed by another girl one year later. All seemed well and, at last, they had the little family they had only previously dreamed about. Margaret developed breast cancer only two years after the adoptions. At home Margaret was managing well, but the girls had become quiet and removed. It was discovered that at their school, other children, after having overheard parents gossiping, were responsible for the girls' change in behaviour. It emerged that their friends had been saying to them, "Your mummy has cancer and she's going to die, isn't she?" As you can imagine the girls were very upset. But the reality was that Margaret was doing well and her situation was being very well managed medically. Margaret spoke at the school assembly and at the parent–teacher meeting. Further, she wrote an article about her situation in the school newsletter. Her trauma became a great learning opportunity for the entire school.

Don't be silent and don't leave your children's emotional health to chance. If you are struggling to communicate or don't know what to say, seek professional help.

Life After Breast Cancer

Post cancer relationships

Maybe you were single prior to breast cancer; perhaps your marriage broke down due to the stress of the illness; maybe you and your existing partner (and carer) have reached a much deeper love and understanding of the other. There are many opportunities for developing "new" relationships; however, some pre-thinking about how you will manage this might be helpful.

For the woman who has had a mastectomy without reconstruction, existing and new relationships can be quite a challenge. It will require a lot of courage, high self-esteem and dogged determination to return to and weave oneself into the relationship market again. There are many ways of handling this part of your life story that are very much dependent upon the type of person that you are. If you were writing a play about your life, how would you view the plot? Would it be a tragedy, a comedy, a drama, a soap opera, a documentary or a sitcom? Throughout your healing process, your story will change because your view of what has happened to you will change. Hopefully, wisdom has followed all of the trauma and woe. This becomes an important point in your life after cancer. How you deliver your story to the world will be reflected in how comfortable you are with your situation, your body image and yourself.

The story of a patient, who had had a mastectomy, who went dancing at the local dance hall reflects this change. The man next to her became very friendly by the end of the night. They had danced together and, sitting on the bench, he had his arm around her shoulder while she was talking to the woman next to her. Happily engaged in conversation, it was sometime before she realised that he was playing with her breast prosthesis! She was able to see this in a comical light that made everyone around her feel easy and comfortable.

I have experienced a similar situation with my *derrière* which is rather rounded and shapely, so I am told. My nerve damage however has left me with a large portion of both buttocks completely numb. One evening after dinner, an admirer became rather friendly and was stroking my *derrière* from behind while I was in conversation with someone else! I couldn't feel a thing! My new partner was a little upset at this, not realising that I had no feeling whatsoever. Fortunately we had a laugh about it afterwards.

If it is a breast or an area of reconstruction and you are comfortable with it, most people will be comfortable with it. People will like you for the qualities you have, rather than the bits and pieces that you may be missing. If they don't, as the old saying goes, "there are plenty more fish in the sea!".

About a Carer — A Story

Sometimes some understanding may be necessary on your part, especially when you meet someone for the first time. You never know his or her history.

David was seeking a partner. One morning he had an idea while reading the dating section in the Saturday newspaper. He decided that he would write a poem to submit to this section of the paper, hoping he would have a substantial cross section of ladies from which he could choose. Apparently, he had more than a hundred replies from lonely and desperate women. One woman who replied sounded very nice on the telephone and so they arranged to meet for coffee. Very soon after they had met, she courageously announced that she had had a mastectomy. He politely left soon after and did not see her again. Now you may be thinking what a scoundrel, what a cad! However, the woman was not to know that David had actually nursed his dying mother after she had experienced a mastectomy many years earlier. Mother had been a **Woman of Silence** and had not told her son, who was in the Navy at the time, that she had breast cancer. By the time he knew, some years later, she had deteriorated and, by then, had widespread secondary breast cancer that ultimately took her life. Mother, for the nicest of reasons, had thought she had shielded her son by being silent. In reality, she had left him with a lot of unfinished business; and a long period of bereavement, mixed emotions and feelings.

Carers, if you have had a partner die as a result of breast cancer, then your self-care will need to be proactive. Bereavement is something that cannot be rushed. The process of grieving takes different paths for different people. Give yourself time and, importantly, don't just get busy and bury your grief. Research tells us that bereaved partners, who have not grieved, are subject to many health problems; usually within eighteen months to two years of their partner dying. It is not easy to start again; remember that you are one of literally hundreds of thousands of people who are experiencing bereavement today. A support group is an ideal way of sharing your loss with people who will understand. A support group will give you a voice and, importantly, can help you in forming new bonds with new friends.

Chapter Eighteen

Breast Cancer: Where is it Going and What Can We Do?

Over the last twenty years the perception of cancer has undergone many changes. The community perspective now oscillates between fear of breast cancer and the sort of acceptance that there are lots of alternative things you can do about it. When I began working with cancer patients nearly thirty years ago at diagnosis there was much doom and gloom. Whereas now, the feedback that I get, is that women are often told by friends: "Don't worry, you'll be right, there's a lot that they can do these days!" Worse still your friends and neighbours all send books and piles of articles downloaded from the internet containing thousands of cancer "cures". They all mean well, but until you are in the shoes of the patient you never know what it feels like to get a diagnosis. With the flood of self-help material and the internet, patients, carers and helping friends are often confronted with a barrage of information to sort through in the pursuit of the magic cure. Other people mean well and it is good to project positive outcomes.

However one of the problems is that this new attitude means that newly diagnosed women are denied the chance to grieve and to express. They now feel that they *have* to be positive. The women's media have also been providing some sound educational ideas on healthy lifestyles and breast cancer success stories. But again, based on patient feedback, these can also set women up for unrealistic goals. Many of my clients are not aware of the different stages and types of breast cancer and the media articles often do not reflect that. We read that someone has survived breast cancer, sometimes reported only a few months after they have had surgery. We also may read that someone died from breast cancer and the information about type, stage etc is so scanty. It seems that in the public perception breast cancer is all the same; just breast cancer. However from the medical point of view the range, the types and stages of breast cancers are extensive, all with differently expected outcomes. Without labeling people, knowing about the different types can be helpful. No wonder there is so much confusion around breast cancer.

Knowledge is a very powerful tool in this scenario as it can help you to make choices based upon the type of tumour that you have. In fact this morning I had a call from a friend. She happened to mention that she had seen a friend Arthur down the street yesterday. Having not seen him or his wife for many months, she asked if they were all right? Arthur, without an alteration in his demeanor said: "Oh yes, Sheila. She's had cancer and had a breast off. They all have it now don't they? She's fine." All very matter of fact! He then went on to talk of other things. My friend's immediate thought after getting over the surprise was "I don't think she's all right!" The second thought was "I wonder why she didn't tell me?"

Diagnostic techniques have also improved dramatically. Figures now reflect that although more women are diagnosed with breast cancer, more women are also surviving it and surviving longer. In the UK the incidence of breast cancer is increasing by two per cent each year but that is balanced out as fewer are losing their lives to it. These figures are based only upon 1999 statistics; the best available to the time of writing in 2003! Treatments also have improved and no doubt the success of Tamoxifen adds significantly to these figures. So people are surviving longer, but what about the quality of life of these survivors. How are they surviving survival? What issues have their time with breast cancer left them with?

Do they have to live on with a life-altering condition that now impacts upon their life quality? How do they deal with recurrences and do they fear recurrences long before they are diagnosed? These issues are not included in cold corridors of statistics but they are important issues to address in a compassionate healing community.

The answer to these questions and the issues of prevention of breast cancer is of interest to me. The life skills methods and ideas for personal exploration and healing that are presented in this book could, if embraced by women, make a huge impact upon the breast cancer statistics. As with diabetes, if you have the gene we know that lifestyle factors can switch it on or off. Cancer is no different. With reference to lifestyle factors I include issues of body, mind, emotion and spirit.

The Three Essential Stages of Healing

Having been a participant on the treadmill of healing I began to think that maybe there was another way; a simpler way. There is so much information. How do you select the right information for you? I have had the advantage of working with more than 10,000 cancer patients, most of whom struggled to incorporate alternative and complementary therapies into their mainstream treatment. I have observed many cancer patients and carers becoming so stressed while trying to de-stress that their life quality suffered as a result of trying too hard to heal.

Rather than emphasising that they should take lots of remedies, vitamins and supplements in the beginning of the cancer journey, my experience has pointed the way towards helping patients to sort out the priorities of their healing. First things first.

These are:

1. To deal with the past and present effects of trauma.
2. Explore emotional healing including healing relationships.
3. Find peace of mind, purpose and meaning in life.

4. Rebuild self-mastery and create spiritual resilience.

Concurrently many patients would have begun orthodox medical treatments, but in some places where the medical system is overloaded such as the NHS in England, these principles ideally could be applied during the lapse time awaiting treatment. These principles are the keys to healing the person rather than treating the cancer itself. It does seem that when patients take charge of their life that their treatments work better and remissions happen.

With these in place I have found that empowered patients will make better choices and more succinct choices as to the therapies that are right for them. Rather than grasping at straws and trying to learn everything as if they had to know it all yesterday. This of course is the recipe for getting stressed while trying to de-stress.

The following is a summary of what I have termed *The Three Stages of Healing*. I have based this information upon both the response from patient surveys and my own experience of walking in the shoes of the patient. I believe that the following principles can be applied in making a treatment plan for any illness.

When first diagnosed with cancer the immediate thought that goes through most people's heads is that cancer can kill you. I might die.

This scenario can trigger:

- A survival response known as the flight or fight response which affects the body's chemistry. It also causes tension in the body.
- Fear is the motivator as a response to the diagnosis. It can either throw you into helpless–hopeless mode and denial, or into fighting mode but all have the same motivator — fear.

We know that this state can either throw a patient into doing too many things at once or the opposite; they give up. This is why intervention for PTSD is so important at the diagnosis time.

Stage one:

Everyone who is diagnosed with a life-threatening illness will go through all or some of the first stage. Ideally, stay in this stage just long enough to make up your mind that you do want to live, then move on. Hence I call this the *will to live stage*. The reasons are outlined below.

When you are in this survival mode, and you have made the decision to "fight", the stages and effects are:

- Confusion — an inability to focus on one thing well.
- You can get into guilt and bargaining — the why me?
- You can lose awareness due to too much trying to "do" and too much "doing".
- You try to heal as of yesterday!
- You use the language of shoulds, musts, dos , don'ts, if only I'd …
- You can become paranoid, neurotic or tunnel visioned and a perfectionist about healing.
- Inflexibility — fear of doing the wrong thing if you believe your life depends upon it.
- All things, including meditation, become a treatment rather than a lifestyle.
- There is a sense of desperation.
- You use up a lot of energy on all levels.

With regard to your body and stress management:

- The resistance or fear of death inhibits getting on with life.
- If *trying* to meditate you are often frustrated because of trying too hard.
- Due to PTSD — in meditation you will sleep, drift and generally "space out".
- Due to lack of connection with the body you will think relaxed but will remain very tense and not notice or be aware of it.
- Get stressed by trying not to stress.

- Personal boundaries are either non existent or you have built "walls".

Stage two:

This stage focuses more on self-discovery. I call it the *will to heal stage*. Ideally this is the stage that is more advantageous to your healing. The only requirement for this stage is that you have chosen life! You want to live well and die well. What more could we want?

In this stage:

- The motivation is different — not initiated by fear or desperation but rather by a desire to search for life meaning.
- What was considered a treatment starts to become a lifestyle.
- You develop intuition, awareness and a belief in yourself to know what is right for you.
- Fear dispels.
- You will consider and take time to make the right choices for you.
- Self mastery begins.
- You begin to rebuild damaged personal boundaries and heal relationships that are significant to you.
- You begin to live well with your illness.
- You practise self-care and begin to prioritise your needs.

Stress Management:

- Mind and body become more congruent.
- Meditation, awareness and mindfulness mean that you begin to "space in" rather than "space out".

Stage three:

By this stage the illness has taken a lesser position in your life.

- You are living very well either with your illness or you may be in remission.

- Mindfulness is a part of your day and meditation flows into your day as well.
- There is innate trust and faith that you will be okay whether you live or die.
- A sense of self-mastery in your life has developed. The struggle has gone.
- Your boundaries are healed and restored allowing you to exude a spiritual resilience and presence that others notice.
- You are living authentically, true to yourself.
- Relationships with those who matter are healed and communication is working for you.
- Life has become easeful.

So we have come to the conclusion of this book. Think carefully about what you have read. How can you apply these principles in your life? Refer to the book and re-read it from time-to-time. It is your handbook to health and healing.

In closing there is one thing that I recommend that you do. Open up a self-care bank account. Into that account each day deposit one thing; just one thing that you can deposit towards your self-care and wellbeing. You can choose all sorts of things. It might be one mindfulness activity, going to Tai Chi, Yoga, Qigong, walking or even having a massage. At the end of the week you will be in credit. At the end of the month your bank balance will be looking good and so on. You can increase the deposits each day when you are ready to. If you keep this bank account in credit you can prevent burnout and enjoy a better level of health. Should a life crisis occur you will have enough credit to make a withdrawal. You see the problem for many of us is that we just keep on going, forget about ourselves and make lots of withdrawals without getting our balance right by making regular deposits. When this happens for long enough, people experience physical, psychological, emotional and spiritual bankruptcy. This is when we are most vulnerable to illness.

Sing your song, dance your dance, heal the old life story, close the chapter and the book and begin your new life. Go well.

Grace Adamson
June 2003

Recommended Reading

Spirituality

Eternal Echoes, John O'Donahue
Bantam (2000) ISBN 0-5538-1241-6
Anam Cara: Spiritual Wisdom from the Celtic World,
John O'Donahue
Bantam (1999) ISBN 0-5535-0592-0
The Tibetan Book of Living and Dying, Sogyal Rimpoche
Harper ISBN 0-0625-0793-1

Emotional and Psychological Healing

Facing Shame: Families in Recovery, Merle Fossum and
Marilyn Mason
Norton (1986) ISBN 0-3933-0581-3
Forgiveness: A Bold Choice for a Peaceful Heart,
Robin Casarjian
Bantam Doubleday ISBN 0-5533-5236-9
*Boundaries and Relationships: Enjoying and Protecting the
Self,* Dr Charles Whitfield
Health Communications (1993) ISBN 1-5587-4259-X
Malignant Sadness: The Anatomy of Depression,
Louis Wolpert
Faber and Faber (2001) ISBN 0-5712-0727-8
A Little Book on the Human Shadow, Robert Bly
Harper and Row (1988) ISBN 0-0625-4847-6

Healing and Cancer

Dr Susan Love's Breast Book, Susan M Love MD
Perseus (2000) ISBN 0-2014-0835-X
The Healing Heart, Norman Cousins
Anatomy of an Illness, Norman Cousins
Head First: The Biology of Hope, Norman Cousins

The Miracle of Mindfulness, Thich Nhat Hanh
Beacon Press ISBN 0-8070-1239-4
Wherever You Go There You Are, Jon Kabat Zin
Full Catastrophe Living, Jon Kabat Zin
The Relaxation Response, Herbert Benson MD
Quill Harper Collins ISBN 0-3808-1595-8
Getting Well Again, Carl O. Simonton
Bantam ISBN 0-5532-8033-3

Women's Wisdom

You Just Don't Understand: Men and Women in Conversation,
Deborah Tannen
Quill ISBN 0-0609-5962-2
Women's Bodies Women's Wisdom, Chris Northrup
Hay House ISBN 0-9459-2340-6
Conscious Femininity, Marion Woodman
Bookworld Services ISBN 0-9191-2359-7
Women Who Run With The Wolves, Clarissa Pinkola Estes
Ballantine Books ISBN 0-3453-9681-2
Molecules of Emotion, Candace Pert
Scribner Book Company ISBN 0-6848-3187-2

Awareness and Healing

The Listening Hand, Ilana Rubenfeld
Bantam Books ISBN 0-5533-7983-6
Silent Spring, Rachel Carson
Penguin ISBN 0-1402-7371-9
Breath, Bone and Gesture — Practices of Embodiment,
Don Johnson
Group West ISBN 1-5564-3201-1
Cancer as a Turning Point, Lawrence Le Shan (video)
Order: New Way, PO Box 8241, Manchester, CT 06040, USA
*Rachel's Daughters: Searching for the Causes of Breast
Cancer* (1997) (video)
Love, Medicine and Miracles, Bernie Seigel (audio)
Harper ISBN 0-8984-5767-X

Resources

The management of cancer and serious illness, using supportive, alternative and complementary care practices, is very specialised. This applies specifically to methods for deep relaxation and meditation.

Many chapters in this book refer to these techniques. Listed below are a number of CDs that have been specifically prepared as a result of working with more than 10,000 patients. They have indicated that the approach and methods suggested in these CDs have been most helpful in their healing process.

The music has been specifically composed for each CD and, rest assured, none of the content is subliminal.

Please visit my website:
www.graceadamson.com
for further information and to place your order.

IMAGINING HEALTH A: A HEALING VISUALISATION JOURNEY

Using music and voice, this is a gently guided visualisation journey focusing upon images of the earth. A non-specific image exercise designed to increase your kinaesthetic awareness which also includes sounds of Australian bush birds and waterfalls with harp and bass recorder.

Level: For beginners and experienced meditators.

IMAGINING HEALTH B: MUSIC ONLY

The same music found on Imagining Health A is used. It is designed so that you can create and experience your own visualisation journey using the music as a guide.

Level: For beginners and experienced meditators.

BEGINNING MEDITATION: OPTIMISING RELAXATION
AND MEDITATION FOR HEALING

This is a spoken presentation that helps to de-mystify
meditation, making the practice more attainable for beginners.
An explanation of how stress impacts on your body as well as
your mind is accompanied by simple awareness exercises that
will help you reach deeper levels of relaxation.

Level: For beginners.

ENTERING THE QUIET PLACE

An instructional relaxation and meditation exercise with harp
and musical accompaniment. This exercise is designed to
assist you to focus your mind during meditation using breath
and personal mindfulness. The exercise will also help you to
stay present and aware throughout.

Level: For all meditators.

WOMEN'S HEALTH SERIES:
A. MEDITATION ON THE FEMININE PRINCIPLE

This guided deep relaxation exercise that emphasizes the
awareness of the feminine; the deep wisdom within. There is
musical accompaniment.

Level: For beginners and experienced meditators.

WOMEN'S HEALTH SERIES:
B. LEARNING TO BE CALM

A guided deep relaxation exercise using progressive muscle
relaxation. By using breath, mindfulness and awareness,
assisted by musical accompaniment, you will experience a far
deeper level of relaxation.

Level: For beginners and experienced meditators.

For all who want to be inspired and spellbound! ...

TAKING THE JOURNEY OF CANCER:
GRACE'S PERSONAL STORY OF HOPE AND RECOVERY

This is an incredible account of the lives of two utterly determined people. This is the inspiring story of the Gawlers told in a very personal and informative way. Now Grace Adamson, she tells her story from the carer's point of view as well as from her own experience as a health professional who then became the patient. This astonishing story highlights key features that will assist anyone who is taking the cancer journey.

An absolute must for anybody dealing with trauma ...

RECONNECTING WITH THE EMOTIONAL HEALING OF CANCER

We examine the cause and effect of emotional issues about quality of life, hope, healing, recovery and survival. When you drop a stone into still water there is a ripple effect — circles radiate out from the point of entry. Many cancer treatments focus on the ripples (cells). We will focus on where the stone is dropped (the person). Practical information and exercises about how to heal the effects of old and current emotional trauma are provided.

An additional resource:

For those interested in training and reading more about *mind–body awareness* please refer to Ilana Rubenfeld's website:
www. ilanarubenfeld.com